Mathematical Aspects of
Marine Traffic

The Institute of Mathematics and its Applications Conference Series

Optimization, *edited by* R. Fletcher
Combinatorial Mathematics and its Applications, *edited by* D. J. A. Welsh
Large Sparse Sets of Linear Equations, *edited by* J. K. Reid
Numerical Methods for Unconstrained Optimization, *edited by* W. Murray
The Mathematics of Finite Elements and Applications, *edited by* J. R. Whiteman
Software for Numerical Mathematics, *edited by* D. J. Evans
The Mathematical Theory of the Dynamics of Biological Populations, *edited by* M. S. Bartlett and R. W. Hiorns
Recent Mathematical Developments in Control, *edited by* D. J. Bell
Numerical Methods for Constrained Optimization, *edited by* P. E. Gill and W. Murray
Computational Methods and Problems in Aeronautical Fluid Dynamics, *edited by* B. L. Hewitt, C. R. Illingworth, R. C. Lock, K. W. Mangler, J. H. McDonnell, Catherine Richards and F. Walkden
Optimization in Action, *edited by* L. C. W. Dixon
The Mathematics of Finite Elements and Applications II, *edited by* J. R. Whiteman
The State of the Art in Numerical Analysis, *edited by* D. A. H. Jacobs
Fisheries Mathematics, *edited by* J. H. Steele
Numerical Software—Needs and Availability, *edited by* D. A. H. Jacobs
Recent Theoretical Developments in Control, *edited by* M. J. Gregson
The Mathematics of Hydrology and Water Resources, *edited by* E. H. Lloyd, T. O'Donnell and J. C. Wilkinson

In Preparation

Mathematical Aspects of Marine Traffic, *edited by* S. H. Hollingdale
Stochastic Programming, *edited by* M. A. H. Dempster
Numerical Methods in Applied Fluid Dynamics, *edited by* B. Hunt
Mathematical Modelling of Turbulent Diffusion in the Environment, *edited by* C. J. Harris
Mathematical Methods in Computer Graphics and Design, *edited by* K. Brodlie
Recent Developments in Markov Decision Processes, *edited by* D. J. White, R. Hartley and L. C. Thomas
Analysis and Optimization of Stochastic Systems, *edited by* O. L. R. Jacobs, M. H. A. Davis, M. A. H. Dempster, C. J. Harris and P. C. Parks

Mathematical Aspects of Marine Traffic

*Based on the Proceedings of the Conference
on Mathematical Aspects of Marine Traffic
held at Chelsea College London in September,
1977, organized by the Institute of Mathematics
and its Applications*

Edited by

S. H. HOLLINGDALE

*Formerly Director of Computer Services,
University of Birmingham,
Birmingham, UK*

1979

ACADEMIC PRESS

London   New York   Toronto   Sydney   San Francisco

A Subsidiary of Harcourt Brace Jovanovich, Publishers

ACADEMIC PRESS INC. (LONDON) LTD.
24/28 Oval Road,
London NW1

United States Edition published by
ACADEMIC PRESS INC.
111 Fifth Avenue
New York, New York 10003

British Library Cataloguing in Publication Data
Mathematical aspects of marine traffic.
(Institute of Mathematics and its Applications.
Symposium proceedings series).
1. Navigation—Mathematics—Congresses
I. Hollingdale, Stuart Havelock   II. Series
623.88′84′0151   VK555   78-66696

ISBN 0-12-352450-4

Printed by W. & G. Baird Ltd.,
at the Greystone Press, Antrim.

CONTRIBUTORS

M.J. BARRATT;*National Maritime Institute, Feltham, Middx.*

J.H. BEATTIE; *Decca Radar Limited, 9 Albert Embankment, London SW1.*

J.E. BURY; *Trinity House, London EC3N 4DH.*

R.L. CLOET; *University of Bath, Claverton Down, Bath, Avon.*

A.N. COCKCROFT; *City of London Polytechnic, 100 Minories, Tower Hill, London EC3N 1JY.*

R.G. CURTIS; *National Maritime Institute, Feltham, Middx.*

A.D. GILL; *National Maritime Institute, Feltham, Middx.*

E.M. GOODWIN; *City of London Polytechnic, 100 Minories, Tower Hill, London EC3N 1JY.*

J.D. GRIFFITHS; *University of Wales Institute of Science and Technology, King Edward VII Avenue, Cardiff CF1 3NU.*

E.R. HARGREAVES; *Formerly of the Department of Trade.*

E.M. HASSAM; *University of Wales Institute of Science and Technology, King Edward VII Avenue, Cardiff CF1 3NU.*

J. HIGGINS; *Liverpool Polytechnic, Byrom Street, Liverpool L3 3AF.*

S.H. HOLLINGDALE; *Formerly of the Royal Aircraft Establishment.*

J. HOLMES; *City of London Polytechnic, 100 Minories, Tower Hill, London EC3N 1JY.*

Y. IIJIMA; *Tokyo University of Mercantile Marine, Japan.*

J. KEARON; *The Salvage Association, Lloyd's Building, London EC3M 7EU.*

J. KEMP; *City of London Polytechnic, 100 Minories, Tower Hill, London EC3N 1JY.*

G.R.G. LEWISON; *National Maritime Institute, Feltham, Middx.*

J.R. MOON; *Liverpool Polytechnic, Byrom Street, Liverpool L3 3AF.*

D. PRANDLE; *Institute of Oceanographic Sciences, Bidston, Observatory, Birkenhead, Merseyside.*

PREFACE

This book contains the 17 papers, revised for publication
where necessary, that were presented at a 2-day conference
held at Chelsea College, London University in September 1977.
The conference was organised by the Institute of Mathematics
and its Applications, in collaboration with several other
organisations, notably the Royal Institute of Navigation and
the National Maritime Institute.

Marine navigation and mathematics have been close part-
ners for centuries. Thus, for example, the Royal Observatory
was established at Greenwich in 1675 for the express purpose
of improving navigation. The first Astronomer Royal was charged
with the task of making the accurate observations of the moon's
motion that were needed to enable mariners to find their longitude at sea. Accurate chronometers did not exist in the 17th
century. Coming to recent times, we find that during the
1960's the main mathematical interest was directed to the problem of collision avoidance. The mathematical studies of this
decade undoubtedly had a significant influence on the revi-
sions of the International Regulations for Preventing Collision
at Sea that were adopted at the 1972 IMCO conference. During
the last few years the focus of attention has moved from a
pair of ships in the open sea to a marine traffic system
involving a number of ships in confined waters.

The post-war growth of marine traffic - in the number,
size, speed and variety of the vessels that make up the
traffic - pointed inexorably to the need for some measure of
traffic control in the more conjested areas. These usually
took the form of a 'linear' routeing scheme (i.e. the separation of opposing traffic streams) as in the Dover Straits.
Sometimes, however, more complex 'areal' arrangements were introduced, as in Tokyo Bay. A feature of all such control
schemes was the extensive use of mathematical models - first
in the planning stage, and then later to assist in evaluating
the practical effect of the scheme and to suggest improvements.
Considerable effort was also devoted to observing what was
actually happening and to collecting information on traffic
flow, ships' behaviour involving close encounters or dangerous
manoeuvres, etc. Such statistical data needed to be analysed

and interpreted. Here again the mathematician was called into
service, with digital computers at hand to take care of the
numerical chores.

Mathematical modelling of selected features of a complex
'real world' situation lies at the heart of most practical
applications of mathematics; the marine traffic field is no
exception. Such models have the great advantage that their
behaviour can be studied for a wide range of values of the
parameters of the model. This means that the effect of changes
in specified features of the situation - such as traffic
density, routeing arrangements or the composition of the traffi
(e.g. more supertankers or hovercraft) - can readily be examined 'on paper'. The contents of this book bear witness to
the importance and versatility of mathematical models in marine
traffic studies, and also to the current pre-occupation with
routeing schemes.

Each of the first four papers may be thought of as
setting the scene in some way, either by presenting an
historical survey or by raising broad issues pertaining to
the main conference themes. We then have three papers dealing
with the collection, analysis and evaluation of statistical
data - on such items as marine casualties or traffic flow.

Then follows a paper on the underwater environment; it
discusses the techniques and pitfalls of charting the ever-
changing shape of the sea bed in confined waters.

The remaining nine papers are concerned with mathematical
modelling. The models range from complex dynamical represent-
ations of the behaviour of a ship when maneouvring to kinematic
models of traffic flow in prescribed streams, designed to predict the frequency of close encounters or collisions of various
types. The four papers from the National Maritime Institute
are especially noteworthy in this context. One paper from the
Institute of Oceanographic Studies discusses hydrodynamic
models for simulating tide and surge propagation in shallow
waters, and their use in providing flood warnings and assist-
ance to shipping.

Two further papers warrant special mention. The first is
Professor Iijima's tantalisingly brief survey of the Japanese
approach to marine engineering - a new discipline which has
been defined as 'the study of marine traffic and the application of the results of such a study to improvements in navigational facilities and traffic regulations,with the aim of

making sea transport both safe and efficient'. (A. Silverleaf
at a conference to introduce the subject of Marine Traffic
Engineering, held at Teddington in 1972; *J. of Nav.*, **25**, p 379.)

The final paper, from the University of Wales Institute
of Science and Technology, is on shipping operations on the
Suez Canal. This fine piece of 'classical' operational research employs the technique of integer linear programming
to good effect. Its most striking conclusion is that the
shipping capacity of the Canal could be increased by more than
40% simply by expanding the cycle time of operations from the
present 24 hours to 48 hours.

I would like to thank the many people who have contributed
to the success of the conference and to the publication of
this book; in particular, the staff of the Institute of Mathematics and its Applications for organising the conference
itself and then the publication of its proceedings, and the
authors of the papers for preparing, editing and correcting
their contributions with such care. It is to be hoped that
some of the younger generation of applied mathematicians will
be encouraged to interest themselves in the rewarding new
field of marine traffic engineering.

S.H. Hollingdale   March 1979

The Institute thanks the authors of the papers, the editor, Dr. S.H. Hollingdale and also Miss J. Fulkes and Mrs. S. Hockett of the IMA for typing the papers for publication.

CONTENTS

MARINE TRAFFIC - THE RÔLE OF GOVERNMENT

E. R. Hargreaves

(Formerly of the Department of Trade)

I shall take as a sort of text for my paper parts of the opening passage of "Murders in the Rue Morgue" by Edgar Allan Poe: "The mental features discoursed of as the analytical are in themselves but little susceptible of analysis. They are always to their possessor when inordinately possessed a source of the liveliest enjoyment. As the strong man exults in his physical strength so glories the analyst in that moral activity which disentangles. The faculty of resolution is much invigorated by mathematical study and especially by that highest branch of it which unjustly and merely on account of its retrograde operations has been called analysis." Allowing for the somewhat strange phrases used by Poe this quotation does I think point the theme of my talk. My subject is the rôle of Government but my theme is the importance of the enthusiastic analyst.

The title of this conference is the mathematical aspects of marine traffic but it is on the safety of that traffic that we are concentrating at this meeting. It is however unfortunately true that Governments (by which I mean Ministers) are, to be honest, not greatly concerned with safety at sea. They are concerned with the safety of the realm against foreign attack, the physical and economic well-being of the citizen, the maintenance of law and order, but only if public opinion forces them to take action, usually after some dramatic casualty, are Ministers willing to give much attention to marine safety.

In this lack of interest they have not always been alone of course. One does not need to watch the Onedin Line to know that shipowners have not always given high priority to safety, nor indeed have the sailors themselves. Perhaps those most concerned until recently have been their wives and mothers,

anxious to see their men home safe from the sea. Now of course
we have the powerful environmental lobbies. Thus advances in
marine safety have owed a great deal to the enthusiast and the
analyst.

    Probably the earliest involvement of British Governments
in legislation on navigation was the system of Navigation Laws
which provided that goods, often wine in the early days, must
be carried in British ships. This was a fine protective system
built up over centuries to encourage our merchant shipping and to
train seamen for a country which had to have a Navy in time
of war but could not, or would not, maintain it in times of
peace. The Navigation Acts passed by Cromwell hit Dutch trade
so badly that they declared war on us. But when Charles II
came back he continued and enlarged the Acts and he also set
up the Royal Observatory, the first subsidised scientific institution in England, very largely to help navigation. But
the Navigation Acts helped to lose us the American Colonies
and proved a protective system of very doubtful value to our
expanding industrial economy of the 19th century. Finally
after rioting had taken place in Trafalgar Square in 1848,
the Navigation Laws were repealed.

    The Board of Trade was naturally the Department that
administered the Navigation Laws and so became the Department
concerned with merchant shipping, although in the early days
it had no responsibility for supervising the safety of ships.
However with trade and emigration increasing rapidly the rate
of shipwreck mounted. By the early 1830's about 900 seamen
were lost by shipwreck each year and indeed in the black
January of 1843 240 ships were wrecked and 500 lives lost
within 3 days. By the 1870's the annual loss of life was
nearly 2000. In 1836 the Government appointed a Select
Committee of the House to enquire into the causes of shipwreck.
The Committee, acting with great speed, produced a report the
same year, only 9 pages long but backed by minutes of evidence
covering 267 pages. The speed of the Committee was not echoed
by Parliament itself but gradually some laws relating to marine
safety were enacted.

    I shall not go into the early stages of these developments
except to mention two enthusiasts. Samuel Plimsoll was the
London coal merchant who took up the cause of the evils of
overloading and went into Parliament, where on one occasion
he was so infuriated by the slowness of the Government of
Disraeli that he called Members of the House villains and shook
his fist in the Speaker's face. For this he had to apologise,

but be finally forced the Government to introduce the Load
Line, the famous Plimsoll line (and I suppose walked the deck
in plimsolls). Thomas Gray entered the Board of Trade as a
clerk in 1851 and became Head of the Marine Department 16 years
later at the age of 37. It was he who took the lead in the
development of Merchant Shipping legislation and, perhaps more
memorably, put the Rules of the Road into rhyming verse, such
as "Green to Green, Red to Red, Perfect safety, go ahead ".

It was almost certainly the loss of the Titanic, with
1489 people drowned, that led to the first International Conference on Safety at Sea in the winter of 1913-1914, and perhaps one should not blame governments for not doing much about
their conclusions. There was a second International Conference
in 1929 and a third in 1948 which established the Intergovern-
mental Maritime Consultative Organisation which now plays the
key rôle in marine safety. It took 10 years however for Governments to ratify the IMCO convention and get the organisation
going, and since then they have been far too slow to ratify
IMCO resolutions and the decisions of international conferences
on maritime matters.

So far, we have looked at the steps taken by Governments
to improve the safety of the ship itself. There was also the
development of the collision regulations to which I have made
passing reference. These regulations always concentrated on
encounters between two ships only, until in Rule 10 of the
latest rules they deal for the first time with traffic separation. So let us turn to another aspect of the development of
Government legislation on shipping, harbour legislation, for it
can be argued that current ideas on the safety of marine traffic
stem just as much if not more from harbour legislation as from
the Merchant Shipping Acts and the Collision Regulations.

The key Act is the Act of 1847 "for consolidating into
One Act certain Provisions usually contained in Acts authoris-
ing the making and improving of Harbours Docks and Piers", -
the Harbours, Docks and Piers Clauses Act of 1847. The Act
set out a very large number of standard provisions which were
then applied to various ports by Private Acts. The provisions
that concern us are those which give Harbour Masters powers "for
regulating the Time at which and the Manner in which any Vessel
shall enter into, go out of, or lie in or at the Harbour".
However this only allowed him to give a direction to a particular ship. If the Master refused he could be fined £20, but
if the Harbourmaster misbehaved his fine was only £5, while
the fine for offering a bribe to him, or for taking such a bribe,

was also £20; and if the Master came into the Dock without his
sails lowered or furled he could be fined £10. Similar provisions about directions to ships were repeated in later Acts
but not until 1964 in Sec. 20 of the 1964 Harbours Act were
more general powers provided by Parliament to control the
movement of ships in harbours, by Control of Movement Orders
made by the Minister on the application of the Harbour Authority. I am told that little or no use has been made directly
of these provisions but the Port of London Act of 1968 provides
for General Directions to Shipping as well as Special Directions
to individual ships. A number of other UK ports also now regulate the movement of shipping by VHF or by other means and
many operate radar surveillance systems.

     The Government has been involved in much of this develop-
ment for which the main impetus has been, I would think, the
efficient and profitable operation of the port rather than
the improvement of safety, though the careful planning of
systems so as to ensure safety owes much to individual enthusiasts, as many of us know.

     The Government has also been deeply involved in legisla-
tion and administration of Pilotage, but that is a separate
subject.

     For the next stage in the improvement of the safety of
marine traffic we again have to turn to the enthusiasts.
Mr. Beattie will describe the development of traffic separation
and routeing; I merely draw your attention to the part played
by enthusiasts and analysts.

     Let us now look at the action that the UK Government took
following the series of accidents in the Channel and Dover
Strait in 1970-71. The collision between the "Pacific Glory"
and the "Allegro" in 1970 south of the Isle of Wight in which
a large amount of oil was spilt and caught fire first alerted
the public to the dangers of the Channel. However, it was
the Texaco Caribbean-Paracas collision on 11th January 1971,
followed the next day by the Brandenburg hitting the wreck
and sinking with all the inevitability of a Classical Greek
tragedy, that really shocked the public, with the modern Greek
tragedy of the Niki striking the wreckage again on 27th February
to emphasise what was described as Channel motorway madness.
Altogether 51 people died in the 3 accidents. Newspapers
carried headlines such as "The Channel Bomb", "The Ship that
Reached out from the Grave", and "The Great Channel Traffic
Jam". On the 13th January the Minister made a long statement

to the House and came under pressure from a number of MPs for controls of various kinds over channel shipping. During the weeks that followed the press and TV gave wide coverage to the problems with interviews with many eminent marine personalities. There were proposals for an International police force to patrol the channel, compulsory pilotage for all ships passing through, the extension of the routeing scheme right down to Lands End with assembly and dispersal points laid down, a reporting system for all ships entering and leaving the Straits, an International Authority to control all aspects of navigation in the channel paid for by fees levied on shipping (thought to be favoured by the French), speed limits and even limitations on the size of vessels with the VLCCs routed round the North of Scotland.

The Government pinned its faith on getting IMCO to persuade all governments to make compliance with the Dover Strait scheme compulsory for its ships. In this it was only partially successful - even the French never did so-though now the new Collision Regulations(Colregs) have achieved the desired results. It examined the possibility of extending territorial limits to 12 miles, but this met with resistance from many quarters, particularly as the Law of the Sea talks were just beginning. It also carried out fresh hydrographic surveys of the area, brought back a SAR helicopter to Manston, and set in train a wide range of research work on the problem. After a study by consultants who sounded nautical opinion very widely, both here and in NW Europe, it also set up the Channel Information Service.

It is difficult now, over 6 years later, to remember the strength of feeling at the time and the flurry of activity. There were urgent meetings with the French Government; the Foreign Office sent cables to posts all over the world to sound out foreign views on compulsory routeing; the most extensive wreck marking ever deployed was provided by Trinity House after discussions with the Secretary of State immediately following the Niki disaster; several meetings of the Department's Safety of Navigation Committee were quickly held and a special Marine Traffic Systems Steering Group was set up in March. Even the Prime Minister was worried. At the beginning of March, he wrote to the Secretary of State's office to express his personal concern and to call for a report the next day on what was being done. The Prime Minister suggested that action through IMCO might not be enough to satisfy the Government's critics and that bilateral action with the French might have to be taken about Channel navigation.

Fortunately there were no further serious collisions that year in the Straits, nor indeed have there been since, though there have been collisions that could easily have been much more serious, and plenty of near misses. This has given time for analysis and study, much of which will be described in later papers, and for the installation of an extensive radar surveillance of the Straits. If however there had been another bad accident in 1971, as many confidently predicted would occur if we did not reverse the routeing or put pilots on every ship, we might well have been driven to take unwise action.

What of the future? There is now a standing Anglo French Safety of Navigation group to coordinate studies and developments, and much remains to be done before the problems are fully understood and solved. Only when they come under heavy pressure from public opinion as a result of major accidents are Governments prepared to legislate. Accidents in Japanese waters led the Japanese Government to introduce its Maritime Traffic Safety Law in 1973; similarly a series of accidents to tankers in US waters, especially the Argo Merchant last year, has stirred President Carter to action; and most recently, after all too many accidents in the Malacca Straits, the 3 coastal states have just tabled at IMCO a comprehensive traffic system for the Straits including a minimum under keel clearance and requirements for reporting to shore controls.

Captain Cockcroft and others will be discussing collision statistics in later papers. One thing of which we can be pretty sure is that the world has not seen the last major collision. Indeed many people expect the collision rate to continue to increase over the next ten years.

My own fear is that Governments, stirred out of their usual lethargy concerning safety at sea by public outcry at the latest accident, will try to introduce laws that are not properly directed at the true causes of accidents because they are not based on sufficient careful analysis. Criticisms of this kind can be made in the three cases I have mentioned, Japan, USA and Malacca, but the proposals for the last two cases are still under discussion internationally and some changes may be made.

In spite of ever more sophisticated Collision Avoidance Radars, as they are hopefully called, human error seems to remain the prime cause of accidents. It is the causes of such errors, and how best to create situations in which errors that do occur can be corrected before it too late and the accident

happens, that now most need further study. The analyst now
has at his elbow modelling techniques and ship simulators to
experiment with. He can try out a wide variety of situations
and study the reaction of the man on the bridge. We know that
80% of collisions occur in high density traffic areas and a
recent study by Captain Lusted shows that 84% of strandings
occurred at night, a much higher proportion than in poor visibility (less than 2 miles). This suggests to my simple mind
that there must be scope for improving safety at night in dense
traffic areas. Perhaps one of you enthusiastic analysts will
come up with the answer. To end as I began with Edgar Allan
Poe: "The analysts results, brought about by the very soul
and essence of method, have in truth the whole air of intuition".

DEVELOPMENT OF SHIPS' ROUTEING 1857-1977

J.H. Beattie

(Decca Radar Limited)

IMCO SHIPS' ROUTEING OBJECTIVES

The original IMCO routeing objective in 1964 was simply to separate traffic at sea. By 1977 no less than seven objectives had been specified:

(i) traffic separation to avoid head-on encounters;

(ii) reducing dangers from crossing traffic and shipping in traffic lanes;

(iii) simplification of traffic patterns in coverging areas;

(iv) organisation of traffic in areas of offshore exploitation;

(v) areas to be avoided by certain ships;

(vi) deep water routes to reduce risk of grounding; and

(vii) guidance of traffic clear of, or through, fishing grounds.

SAFETY AT SEA LEGISLATION AND SHIPS' ROUTEING

The Collision Regulations, or Rule of the Road, first came into force in this country in 1863 and have been changed by successive international Safety Conferences and Conventions between 1897 and 1972. In 1863 the British decided to withdraw the first rule of traffic separation, that of keeping to the Starboard Hand of Narrow Channels, hoping that this would be covered by local rules. The result was a disastrous collision with the loss of 640 lives on September 8th, 1878, in the River Thames - so the rule was brought back again, but after the accident.

At present the International Legislation covering Routeing is by SOLAS 60 and the 1972 Collision Regulations. When it is ratified SOLAS 74 will replace SOLAS 60. Table I shows the current state of such legislation. It will be seen that many of the critical amendments to SOLAS 60 have still not been ratified - the 1971 A.205 on routeing, for example. However, this has been overtaken by events by the important new Rules 1(d) and 10 of the 1972 Collision Regulations which came into force on July 15th, 1977.

Table I

International Legislation and Ships' Routeing IMCO SOLAS Conventions

Legislation	Number of Countries to Establish ratification	Acceptances (as at 1.7.77 unless otherwise stated)
SOLAS 1960 (N. Atlantic Routes-Regulation 8)	15	97 (1.9.65)
AMENDMENTS		
1968 Resolution A.146 (Charts)	64	36
1969 Resolution A.174 (Navaids)	64	25
1971 Resolution A.205 (Routeing)	64	14
SOLAS 1974 (Routeing-Regulation 8)	25	8
AMENDMENTS	Tacit Acceptance	
IMCO RECOMMENDATIONS		
1971 Resolution A228 (Routeing)	-	-
1975 Resolution A340 (Fairways, Safety Zones)	-	-
1975 Resolution A341 (Fairways, Safety Zones)	-	-
IMCO COLLISION REGULATIONS		
1960 Annex B to SOLAS 60	Individual	73 (1.9.65)
1972 Rules 1(d) and 10 on Traffic Separation	15	45 (15.7.77)

TRAFFIC GROWTH

Traffic has grown enormously, particularly since 1960 (Fig. 1). The introduction of traffic separation in 1967 was just in time!

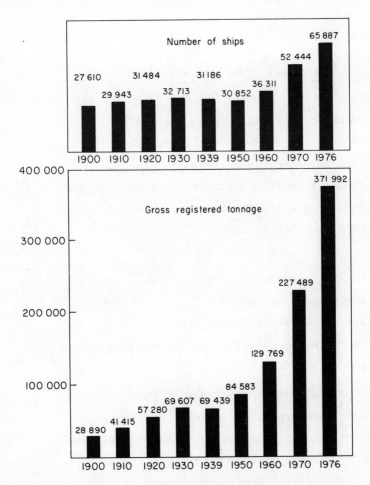

Fig. 1   Growth of world shipping

NEW RISKS

A succession of accidents, mainly to tankers such as the Torrey Canyon, has focused attention on new risks, particularly those involving VLCC's.

INTERNATIONAL SOLUTIONS TO NAVIGATIONAL PROBLEMS

An examination of the history of routeing and hydrography in the last 150 years indicates that significant progress has only been made by international cooperation. This has resulted in the growth of International Marine Organisations, which is summarised in Table II.

Table II

Growth of International Organisations

IMCO

1948 UN Maritime Conference to form IMCO

1958 IMCO established (21 nations accepted)

1959 IMCO 1st Assembly Meeting

1964 IMCO 1st Traffic Separation scheme accepted

1977 IMCO 62 Traffic Separation schemes accepted

      IMCO accepted by 103 nations

IHO

1919 1st IH Conference

1921 IHB founded at Monaco

1967 9th IH Conference forms IHO

      IHO to be responsible for routeing on charts

1970 IHO established

OTHER INTERNATIONAL MARINE ORGANISATIONS

1921 ICS   (International Chamber of Shipping)

1928 CIRM   (Comité International Radio Maritime)

1932 ITU   (International Telecommunications Union)-(Non-Marine)

1955 IAPHA (International Association of Port and Harbour Authorities)

1957 IALA   (International Association of Light house Authorities)

1970 IMPA   (International Maritime Pilot's Association)

1973 IFSMA (International Federation of Shipmasters' Association)

1975 IAIN   (International Association of Institutes of Navigation)

EARLY DEVELOPMENT OF SHIPS' ROUTEING

Perhaps the father of it all was Lt. Maury U.S.N.   The
first of the many notable things he did was to produce Wind
and Current Charts for the North Atlantic in 1847.   In 1855
he proposed in his Sailing Directions that there should be two
separate traffic lanes in the North Atlantic.   Twenty-two years
later Cunard introduced prescribed tracks on the North Atlantic
with evasive routeing south of the Ice.   In 1898 most of the
companies running passenger liners signed the private North
Atlantic Track Agreement, which is referred to in SOLAS 1960.
In this way it became possible to introduce traffic separation
in the 1960's.   However, its application was very limited; in
1960 it only covered 73 ships and was withdrawn recently.

The next most important step in routeing, and indeed the
fore-runner of it all, was the Great Lakes Traffic Separation,
first introduced in 1911 on Lakes Huron and Superior after 22
disastrous collisions between 1900 and 1910.   This compulsory
traffic separation has been very successful indeed.

WARTIME ROUTEING

In World War 1 and World War 2 minesafe routes were introduced by the British and Germans.   After the war the Admiralty
organised these with their NEMEDRI (Northern European and
Mediterranean Routeing Instructions).

There were very extensive NEMEDRI routes in and around the
Great and Little Belts in the Baltic.   Another such route
covered the North Sea coasts of Germany and Holland - an area
where the collision record during the period 1959-1964 was
particularly bad, mainly due to bad navigation.   Operation
NEPTUNE - the invasion of Normandy in 1944 - produced the most
complex routeing plan of all time.   Some 7000 ships were involved and so complex were the arrangements that Mickey Mouse
diagrams had to be produced for each hour or so of the landing
to explain the situation to Captains.   Accuracy of navigation
was paramount, and Decca Navigator and sonar transponders were
used for the first time.

MODERN TRAFFIC SEPARATION

After the Andrea Doria/Stockholm collision in 1956 a number
of French, Belgian and Spanish navigators proposed various
schemes for traffic separation.   In 1961 the combined British,

Table III

Growth of Traffic Separation Schemes

	IMCO and National Schemes				National Schemes	
	1967	1971	1976	1977		1977
Baltic Sea	–	11	15	17	2	1 Russian / 1 Polish
Arctic and White Sea	–	–	–	9	9	5 Russian / 4 Norwegian
W. Europe	1	26	29	29		
Mediterranean	–	3	4	4		
Black Sea	–	–	3	6	6	6 Russian
Indian Ocean	–	14	5	6	2	1 Egyptian / 1 Saudi Arabian
Far East	–	–	9	12	10	1 Singapore / 1 Hong Kong / 5 Japanese / 3 Russian
USA W. Coast	–	2	5	5	3	3 American
USA E. Coast	–	3	5	6		
Canada and NF	–	–	7	7	6	6 Canadian
S. America	–	–	–	6	6	6 Chilean
TOTAL	1	59	82	107	44	

French and German Institutes formed the first Working Group
to establish a plan for the Dover Strait. The plan was made
by seamen after consultation with seamen and was brought into
force through IMCO in 1967. A second working group in 1964
proposed schemes elsewhere in Europe to which IMCO agreed.

Table III shows the growth to 1977 when there were 107
schemes in operation worldwide. 63 of these were IMCO schemes
wholly in international waters and 44 were national schemes
within the territorial seas of individual nations.

DEEP WATER ROUTES

The advent of the deep draught vessel in the early 1960's
posed a new routeing problem. Fig. 2 shows how the draught
of vessels has increased enormously in recent times and how
it became necessary to increase the Survey Danger Line to cope
with this increase.

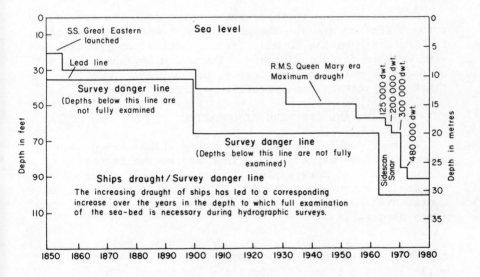

Fig. 2

Table IV shows the growth in the 1970's of Deep Water Routes
which are specially and accurately surveyed to known depths
with instruments such as Side Scan Sonar.

Table IV
Growth of Deep Water Routes

	1971	1973	1975	1977
Baltic Sea	–	–	3	3
North Sea	–	3	4	4
Malacca Strait	–	–	–	1*
Uraga Channel	1*	1*	1*	1*
TOTAL	1	4	8	9

* Not IMCO Schemes

SHIP ROUTEING AND FISHING

Another problem is to devise evasive routeing around and through fishing areas. The artificial concentrations of fishing craft on the 12 mile fishing limits can pose an awkward problem for the planners. These limits, which are set by separate national legislation, may actually come into conflict with international traffic separation schemes.

SHIP ROUTEING AND OFFSHORE EXPLORATION

Another problem is the routeing of ships through and around offshore exploration. This may be the biggest problem in the future as more exploration takes place on the Continental Shelf, which occupies around 7½% of the Oceans, and on the Continental Slope outside that, which occupies an area about twice as great.

As an example let us consider Louisiana and Texas on the U.S. Continental Shelf. By 1975 there were 2839 fixed oil wells and 98 mobiles off Louisiana and Texas. Three U.S. Departments are involved: the Bureau of the Interior sells the real estate: next, curiously the Department of the Army issues drilling permits; and last, the Department of Transportation is responsible for over-all safety. In this case the U.S. Army delineated the shipping Safety Fairways after the drilling had taken place. They are now responsible for stopping obstructions to navigation out to the edge of the Continental Shelf and they delineate a fairway by not granting drilling permits in the fairway.

The Fairways off Louisiana are only 2 miles wide, to accommodate oil drilling requirements, and accuracy of navigation
is essential. Two ships collided with platforms in 1975 so
it is understandable why the USCG is calling for mandatory
position finding equipment. The next major problem is over
delineating North Atlantic Fairways off New York where drilling
may start soon.

HAS SHIPS' ROUTEING BEEN A SUCCESS?

Table V summarises the great success of traffic separation.
Some 150 collisions at sea might have been saved between meeting
vessels in 7 years, before routeing was compulsory. However,
the problems of collisions between crossing, overtaking and
other types of encounters in traffic separation schemes have
yet to be solved.

Table V

Success of Traffic Separation 1967-74

Worldwide in Traffic Separation Areas

Period	Collisions Between Meeting Vessels	Other Collisions
1959-66	264	160
1967-74	115	160
Reduction	56%	Nil

Source: Cockcroft-Statistics of Collision at Sea (1977)

CONCLUSION

The objectives of Ships' Routeing are now so diverse that
the main problems are to be found in the fields of education,
training and communication. Since 1967, 40 papers on marine
traffic and accidents have been published in the *Journal of
the Royal Institute of Navigation*; 16 of them on the Dover
Strait. Since 1973 most of them have concentrated on the mathematical aspects, which is where efforts are increasingly being
concentrated.

THE PRACTICAL BACKGROUND: SETTING THE SCENE

J. E. Bury

(Trinity House, London)

The proposed purpose of the Conference, as I understood
it, was to make a mathematical model of the movement and inter-
relationship of vessels using the Channel and, in particular,
the concentration in the Dover Strait.

I questioned whether this could be done, observing that
no data existed prior to the introduction of the present
Traffic Separation Schemes to provide a comparison. I felt
that one can only make a model of movement when natural forces
are operating, not when they are under constraint.

When setting up a hydraulic model you create the existing
situation as accurately as possible before developing the
pattern of variability you are seeking to introduce. In a
mathematical model (the example I am familiar with is the
"steel mill") the values of some items of input are known and
the effect of variation in each of the others can be calculated.

No such tidy package exists in shipping; the navigation
of a ship is an intensely personal affair, personal to the
Master in particular and to a lesser extent his officers.
Not only are the ships all different but the men in charge of
them are all different; different in background, experience,
attitude and temperament, yet out of all this pot-pourri of
variables in innate and acquired skills there is distilled
what is known as the "ordinary practice of seamen". This is
difficult to quantify, intangible in its application, but real
enough to those who live with it throughout their professional
lives. It is really a form of professional self-discipline
that takes account of the effect of your presence upon the
other ship, but how you quantify that in a mathematical form,
I know not.

When the "natural forces" I mentioned earlier were the
only constraints on movement that existed, mariners were bound

by the ground rules imposed by the Rule of the Road, the
shelter or lack of it provided by land or other natural features, the effect of weather, tides and currents. They were
influenced too, by listening to the experiences of others;
certain fleets had codes of practice not generally observed,
masters had their own preferences which they drummed into their
officers but, in the end, everyone was practising in effect
what we know today as "Traffic Separation".

      Well, having questioned whether a valid traffic model
could be constructed I was asked to "set the scene" of how
it used to be in the English Channel when these natural forces
were operating. Although it is 15 years since I commanded a
ship, part of my work at Trinity House is to recommend the
placing or movement of seamarks and for this I have to apply
the hard won lessons of yesteryear updated by observation and
information.

      Before the advent of radar, the disciplines imposed upon
navigators were severe. You relied upon your eye, efficient
dead reckoning, the correct recognition of other ships and
interpretation of their presence, the occasional direction
finding bearing (R.D/F) given to you by a shore station. Ship-
borne D/F in its infancy had squirrel cage aerials, then came
fixed and rotating loop aerials. The latter were very good
and I learnt the art of D/F fixing with the rotating loop with
the Anchor Line when on the Bombay Mail Service and on a fixed
loop with The New Zealand Shipping Company. This "art" is
one that is not taught in the navigation schools nor at sea
and more's the pity because the D/F can be your best friend
if properly used.

      The D/F beacons in the Channel used to be grouped on a
random basis and I accept that it was difficult to obtain good
"cuts" quickly when you had to re-tune in the middle of a
series. However, I have been instrumental in having all the
D/F beacons in this area re-grouped so that any sequence of
three in a group of six gives an immediate "cut" of three.
This is especially valuable with the new automatic D/F sets.
So, landfalls from the west were by D/F, either shore based
or ship-borne, sun or star sights and visual identification
of lights - if the weather was clear. More often than not in
these waters if you can see two miles you consider yourself
lucky and call it a fine day.

The choice of route in the English Channel was largely
dictated by weather, the dirtiest weather was from the S.W.
and the strongest winds came when the gales veered to the N.W.
In anti-cyclones you could expect visibility to be reduced
by industrial or heat haze and various degrees of fog.

So, coming up Channel, the Mariner sought the English
side where he found a steep-to coast with few off-lying dangers,
no shoals of any significance and very conspicuous and powerful lighthouses. There were also areas under the lee of head-
lands where the smaller ships could anchor in safety and wait
for the gales to blow themselves out; the Downs, Start Point
and Penzance Bay are good examples.

When Southbound in the North Sea you used the various
Light Vessels, soundings of Brown Ridge, your own D/F or else
Radio D/F bearings from North Foreland and a landfall there,
if in doubt passing between the South Falls and the Goodwins,
or else a well worn prayer mat if you elected to go further
South and rely upon sighting the South Foreland light in good
time to go through the South Falls/Sandettie passage on a
bearing.

The next controlling factor was the Rule of the Road.
The astute mariner always saw to it that he always had "good
water" to starboard so that he could alter out of trouble and
not into it (e.g. running along the 10 fathom line from Royal
Sovereign to Dungeness when the cruising pilot cutter was
there.)

We were taught never to go inside the 10 fm. line unnece-
ssarily in these waters or indeed elsewhere in the world, on
the grounds that a prudent seaman should stay in a sufficient
depth of water to allow his draught of ship to pass safely
over an unknown wreck.

The wisdom of this was highlighted when the wreck of
the "Gold Coin" was "found" by a P and O ship a few years
ago. The "Gold Coin" foundered in very bad weather, a garbled
distress was heard by St. Catherine's and North Foreland
Coastal Radio Stations but no position was decipherable. Some
time later an inflatable raft was picked up off Dover which
contained three bodies that were identified as belonging to
that ship. So vague was the information and so bad was the
weather that Trinity House had great difficulty in knowing

B

where to even begin searching.

Many months later a P and O ship reported striking wreckage in a position on the Shingle Bank about 5 miles East of
the Royal Sovereign.   The report was investigated immediately
and a diving inspection identified the "Gold Coin".   The depth
was 9 fathoms!

The advent of radar has removed one of the greatest in-
hibitions to navigation.   A mariner can now "see", albeit
electronically, at greater ranges and with greater accuracy
than anyone would have imagined possible.   Thus the postwar
navigator has been freed from the constraint of having to seek
an early landfall and in consequence his navigation has become
more far-ranging than hitherto.   This is a mixed blessing
really as the increased use of radar and electronic navigation
systems has meant that ships no longer sail on approximately
parallel tracks on well defined trade routes but on divergent
ones that cause ships to "open" or "close" on one another at
relatively fine angles, i.e., the former stratification of
traffic which was a help to the inexperienced has given way
to entrepreneur navigation requiring a much higher standard
of watchkeeping and traffic judgement.

POSTSCRIPT

We all watched with interest the Coastguard film on
traffic movement in the Dover Strait shown at the beginning
of the Conference.   Mr. Hargreaves was at pains to point out
the six "rogues" who had been fishing in the Separation Zone
between Dover and Calais before heading back for Boulogne.
The term "rogues" is Coastguard parlance for anyone who dis-
obeys their political "diktat."   In this case these terrible
"rogues" steamed S.E. against the stream of traffic heading
N.E. in the lane off the French Coast.   May I point out that
they kept to the starboard side of that lane, that they were
wholly inhibited from crossing it ahead of that traffic because
any alteration to port would bring them to a "give way to starboard" situation according to the Steering and Sailing Rules.
They crossed the lane only when it was safe to do so and only
when the opposing traffic permitted.   In short, they compiled
with the Rule of the Road according to the ordinary practice
of seamen.

CAN MATHEMATICS HELP THE MARINER?

S. H. Hollingdale

(Formerly of the Royal Aircraft Establishment)

HISTORICAL

Mathematical techniques have been applied to the problems of marine navigation ever since men first began to sail the open seas. Indeed until comparatively recently, the only way of finding one's position at sea was to observe the movements of the heavenly bodies. When the Royal Observatory was set up at Greenwich in the seventeenth century, it was naturally placed under the jurisdiction of the Board of Admiralty. At that time, in the absence of reliable timekeepers, a solution of the longitude problem was held to require extremely accurate observations of the motion of the moon continued over at least a complete lunar cycle of 19 years. This the first Astronomer Royal, John Flamsteed, set out to provide. No less a mathematician than Isaac Newton spent much of his adult life, even into his old age, wrestling with that most intractable of problems, the theory of lunar motion. His incessant demands for more observational data certainly strained his relations with Flamsteed.

In his later years Newton, as "perpetual" President of the Royal Society, was the Governments *de facto* Chief Scientific Adviser. His opinion on the longitude problem, in particular, was often sought. He had strong views on the subject; this is what he said in 1715 (Hall and Tilling (1976)): "It (i.e., the longitude) is not to be found by Clock-work alone. Clock-work may be subservient to Astronomy but without Astronomy the longitude is not to be found. Exact instruments for keeping of time can be usefull only for keeping the longitude while you have it. If it be once lost, it cannot be found again by such instruments. Nothing but Astronomy is sufficient for this purpose".

So even the most eminent of advisers can misjudge the future - especially when advising the British Government at the age of 72! Newton's great authority undoubtedly contributed

to the official distrust of chronometers from which poor
William Harrison was to suffer so much later on.

The Nautical Almanac was first produced by Neville
Maskelyne - the fifth Astronomer Royal and an ancestor of the
famous magician - in 1767 and has been published annually ever
since. The theory of map making - the representation of part
of a spherical surface on a plane - provides another familiar
example. Many more could be cited.

THE MATHEMATICAL MODEL

The historic debt of the mariners to mathematics is generally accepted. What, however, is the situation today, when
we have radio time signals, computers, electronic aids of all
kinds? The variety and range of the papers presented to this
Conference certainly suggests that mathematics is being applie
to the marine traffic problem at many different points. The
most important single technique used in such applications is
known as mathematical modelling. One constructs a mathematica
model of the traffic situation, and then studies the propertie
of the model in order to obtain some insight into the behaviou
of the "real" situation being modelled. A mathematical model
consists, not of bits of hardware, but of sets of equations,
inequalities and logical connectives. We evaluate its performance by solving the equations, etc., either by using the trad
tional techniques of the mathematician or, nowadays most likel
with the help of a computer to take care of the numerical chor
Indeed, all applied mathematics is essentially an exercise in
model making.

A model, like a map, must drastically simplify the real
situation. Much of the art of modelling lies in knowing what
to put in and what to leave out. While the advent of the computer has shifted the balance between verisimilitude and solv-
ability, the essential skills of the modeller's craft have
remained substantially unchanged.

COLLISION AVOIDANCE

Let us now turn to some of the mathematical studies -
using only elementary mathematics - of marine problems that
have been made during the last 20 years. During the first
half of this period the centre of interest, at any rate in the
United Kingdom, was in how to avoid collision at sea. The
instigator - and chief advocate - of what came to be known as
the mathematical or geometrical approach to collision advoidan

was Dr. Edward Calvert, who described himself as a "human factors engineer" and worked at the Royal Aircraft Establishment, Farnborough.

The collision problem is an annoying one in that it stubbornly refuses to go away. Each year some 7% of the world's ships (excluding small craft) is involved in a collision (Richey (1970). Some 20 years ago, people began to ask whether the Collision Rules - the International Regulations for Preventing Collision at Sea - were adequate in modern conditions.

It will be convenient at this point to quote a few sentences from a Report drawn up in 1970 by Michael Richey, the Executive Secretary of the Royal Institute of Navigation. This Report presented the British view - or to be more precise, the views of a working party set up by the Institute to prepare for an international conference on the Revision of the Collision Regulations that was to meet in 1972. The Report comments: "Informed opinion at sea is nowadays, by and large, critical of the Rules as they stand". (They date essentially from the nineteenth century, before such things as hovercraft or supertankers were thought of.) The Rules lay down that, in most situations, one ship has the responsibility of keeping out of the way of the other (the "privileged ship"), which is to take no action, i.e., is to maintain course and speed. As the Report puts it: "The present Regulations largely ignore the geometry of the situation, and impose on the privileged vessel in an encounter an inertia which sacrifices her ability to contribute to the avoiding maneouvres".

Later on we read: "Discussion within the Institute of Navigation on the revision of the Regulations has gone on, in the Journal and at meetings, over the last fifteen years and many useful studies of the problem have been undertaken, some indeed of a fundamental nature. The most significant contributions have probably been those which centred around the mathematical approach to the subject, and here the extensive work on collision avoidance undertaken by the Mathematics Department of the Royal Aircraft Establishment was first applied to the marine case".

The Report sums up the situation in 1970 thus: "To ignore the geometry of collision as though it had no significance is to put one's head in the sand. The concepts are perhaps difficult and unfamiliar and initially the ideas advanced by Calvert, Hollingdale and others were received almost with incredulity by the marine world, reared perhaps on the immutability of the

Regulations. But over the last decade the climate of opinion
in this regard has considerably changed and it is now generall
accepted that as world shipping develops a far more rigorously
mathematical approach to the collision problem may well be
necessary". The judicious statement that the mathematical
approach was "received almost with incredulity by the marine
world" is no more than the sober truth. Looking back on those
sometimes turbulent confrontations one is astonished at the
extent to which marine opinion has shifted in the course of
a very few years. The recent changes in the Collision Regulations reflect this shift, at any rate in part.

     What, then, are the essential features of the so called
geometrical approach of 1960 to the ship collision problem?
We must first formulate a simple mathematical model, so let us
consider two ships, A and B, on a collision course. Either
one or both ships must take evasive action. Ideally, the
mariner would like to have a single, simple set of rules that
would cover all cases of danger. To what extent can we satisf
him? It seems reasonable to postulate that any scheme of anti
collision maneouvres should satisfy the following requirements

(1)   Each vessel must make a positive contribution to the safe
of the encounter. This means that the effect of action by one
ship cannot be cancelled out by the action of the other. The
two contributions must be additive.
(2)   A mariner must be able to decide on his course of action
on the basis of information that is readily available to him.
This means essentially the relative bearing of the threat vess
not its true motion (speed and heading).
(3) All vessels must be able to operate in accordance with the
same set of rules, i.e. must be able to use a standard diagram
showing the prescribed maneouvres as a function of relative
bearing only.

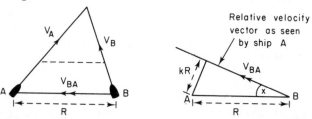

Fig. 1   (a) **Collision situation** (b)   Situation giving a miss
                                            distance of kR

Fig. 1 (a) shows two ships A and B (with speeds V_A and V_B) on a collision course. For this to be the case, each ship must be approaching the other on a <u>constant bearing,</u> so that the sight line (i.e. the line joining the two ships) is moving parallel to itself. This means that the direction of the <u>relative velocity vector</u> (denoted by V_{BA}) remains parallel to the sight line. If the two ships are not a collision course, the relative velocity vector will be inclined to the sight line, say at an angle x when the range is R, as shown in Fig. 1 (b). The <u>miss distance</u> will be kR, where k = sin x.

Now any maneouvre by either ship to avoid collision will cause the sight line to rotate either in a clockwise or an anti-clockwise direction; there is no other possibility. The Collision Regulations give preference to anti-clockwise rotation. Let us therefore adopt this convention, and postulate that each vessel shall maneouvre so that, <u>if the other vessel takes no action</u>, the sight line will always rotate in an anti-clockwise direction. This postulate, which expresses the basic principle of the geometrical approach to collision avoidance, was first enunciated by Calvert (1960). Its significance lies in the fact that it enables each of our three requirements to be met.

Let us now simplify our model a bit more and assume that both vessels take evasive action at the same time, when the range is R, and that this action takes the form of sharp, instantaneous changes of course (a turn) without changes of speed. The combined maneouvres of the two ships have the effect of converting the collision situation of Fig. 1 (a) into that of Fig. 1 (b), and of creating a miss distance of kR = R sin x - or more strictly, as we shall see shortly, a miss distance of at least R sin x.

With these assumptions, it turns out that we can devise, for any specified value of k or x, a manoeuvring diagram, equally applicable to both vessels, that satisfies all our requirements. Furthermore, the diagram is unique (Hollingdale (1961)). As an illustration, Fig. 2 shows such a diagram for the case of k = ½ or x = 30°.

It is not possible in this paper to go through the analysis in detail, but we shall indicate the main steps in the argument.

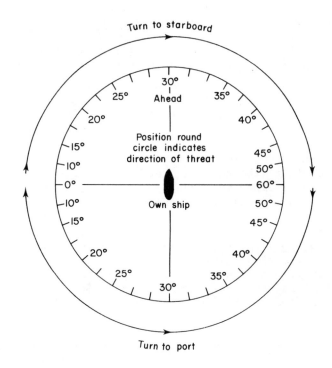

Fig. 2   Turning diagram to produce a miss distance of at leas
          half the range at which course is altered, if both
          ships maneouvre

        Figs. 3 (a) and (b) show the velocity vector triangles
before and after the combined manoeuvre. The initial relativ
bearings of the two vessels are θ_A and θ'_B as shown. When the
range is R, ship A makes a sharp turn to starboard through an
angle ϕ_A and ship B a turn through angle ϕ_B, in both cases
without change of speed. The relative velocity vector rotate
through an angle x, so we have

$$\frac{V_A}{V_B} = \frac{\sin \theta'_B}{\sin \theta_A} = \frac{\sin (\theta'_B + \phi_B - x)}{\sin (\theta_A - \phi_A + x)} \ .$$

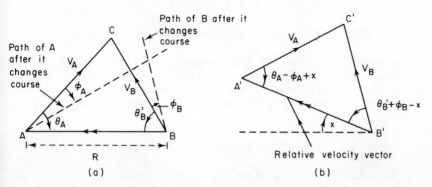

Fig. 3   The situation before and after collision avoidance
         action

   We want to measure all angles positive in a clockwise
direction, so we must set $\theta_B = 360° - \theta_B'$, giving

$$\frac{\sin (\theta_A - \phi_A + x)}{\sin \hat{\theta}_A} = \frac{\sin (\theta_B - \phi_B + x)}{\sin \theta_B}. \tag{1}$$

The symmetry of the result enables us to write

$$\frac{\sin (\theta - \phi + x)}{\sin \theta} = P(x) \tag{2}$$

where θ and ϕ refer to either vessel.

   For a prescribed value of x (i.e., a prescribed value of
the miss distance as fraction of the range at which evasive
action is taken), this equation gives, for either vessel, the
angle of turn, ϕ, as a function only of the relative bearing,
θ.

   We must now determine the form of $P(x)$. To do this we
invoke our basic principle - that each ship must always make
a positive manoeuvre, i.e., one that will cause the sight line
to rotate in an anti-clockwise direction. Now it turns out
(Hollingdale (1961)) that this condition leads to the result
that $P(x)$ must be equal to $\cos x$. Any other value would cause
the anti-clockwise rotation principle to be violated in certain
circumstances. The basic equation from which all maneouvring
diagrams such as Fig. 2 are constructed thus becomes

$$\sin (\theta - \phi + x) = \sin\theta \cos x, \tag{3}$$

and each ship must turn to starboard.

However, this result only applies when the threat to each ship comes from the forward semicircle, as in Fig. 3. If the threat to one ship, say A, comes from astern, we find (Hollingdale (1961)) that this ship must turn to port and the governing equation is

$$\sin (\theta - \phi - x) = \sin\theta \cos x. \tag{4}$$

A further difference is that the miss distance created by executing the manoeuvres presented by equations (3) and (4) is not exactly R sin x, as in the threat-ahead case, but is always greater than R sin x, thus providing an additional margin of safety. Fig. 2, which shows ϕ as a "round the clock" function of θ, is derived from these two equations with x = 3C

Our model is, of course, greatly oversimplified. Its merit is that it can be analysed in detail. The significant result is that in this simple case, the manoeuvres we have described are the only ones that meet all the requirements.

The next step ,clearly, was to examine the effects of re-laxing some of the rather fierce assumptions that had been made so far. During the 1960's quite a lot of work was done on the effect of allowing changes of speed as well as of dir-ection, of taking account of a ship's finite turning circle, of executing the manoeuvres at different times, and - perhaps most important of all - of having to rely on imperfect infor-mation, and especially of the effect of errors in assessing the rate of change of relative bearing and so of miss distance

TRAFFIC SYSTEM STUDIES

By the end of the 1960's the focus of interest had shifte from a pair of ships in splendid isolation to a traffic systen typically to a number of ships in confined waters such as the Dover Strait. In this situation it is important not only to make an evasive manoeuvre where necessary, but also to get the ship back to its original course as soon as it is safe to do so. We need a model that will give us information on how the encounter is developing through time. In 1973 Calvert address himself of this question and showed that the miss distance, M, after both ships have resumed their original courses after completing their manoeuvres can be expressed as

$$M = m + k_A V_A t_A + k_B V_B t_B \qquad (5)$$

where m is the initial miss distance; V_A and V_B are the speeds of the two ships, A and B; t_A and t_B are the lengths of time during which the ships hold their new courses; and k_A and k_B are non-dimensional rate factors, one for each ship.

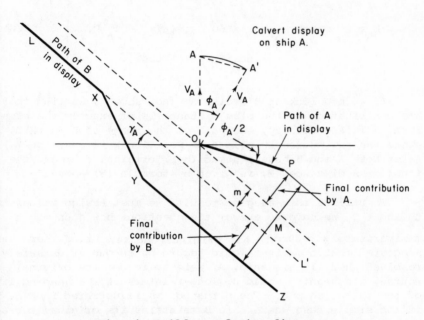

Fig. 4 Build up of miss distance

Fig. 4 shows how such an encounter would be presented on a display on ship A in which the frame of reference is stabilised to move with the velocity (speed and direction) of ship A <u>before</u> manoeuvre. (This form of presentation is known as the "Calvert display". It is very useful, conceptually, for analysing the effect of a combined manoeuvre, since each ship's contribution is shown separately.) Before the start of manoeuvre, the image of ship A on the display remains at rest at the origin, O, while the image of ship B moves along the line LL'. The angle γ_A is the angle which this line makes with the port beam direction of ship A, measured positive as shown.

If A turns to starboard through an angle ϕ_A without change of speed, the image of A will move along the line OP with a speed of $2V_A \sin\phi_A/2$. (OAA' is an isosceles triangle and OP is parallel to AA'.) Once ship A returns to its original course, its image will once again come to rest on the display. If A holds its new course for a time t_A and then returns to its original course, its final image will be at the point P as shown, where OP = $2V_A \sin\phi_A/2 \cdot t_A$. The contribution of A's manoeuvre to the final miss distance will be OPsin $(\gamma_A - \phi_A/2)$ or

$$\left.\begin{array}{l} k_A v_A t_A \text{ where } k_A = 2 \sin\phi_A/2 \cdot \sin(\gamma_A - \phi_A/2) \\[2mm] \qquad\qquad = \cos(\phi_A - \gamma_A) - \cos\gamma_A. \end{array}\right\} \qquad (6)$$

If we now look at B's display (not shown), we find that B's contribution to the miss distance is of exactly the same form. (In A's display, the path of the image of B is LXYZ, where the new course is held from position X to position Y.) After both A and B have resumed their original courses, the final miss distance, M, is given by formula (5) above.

To utilise this elegant result, we must assign values to t_A and t_B. We have to answer the question: how soon may a mariner safely return to his original course? Dr. J. Kemp has suggested that a mariner would regard an encounter as safely resolved when, if his ship, A, were to resume its original course, its heading would no longer intersect the heading line of the threat ship B. The situation is illustrated in Fig. 5 in the simple case where ship B maintains its original course and speed throughout the encounter.

Initially ship A is on course AC and ship B on course BC where AC = a, BC = b, AB = r and angle ACB = α. At time O sh A makes a sharp turn to starboard through angle ϕ. Thereafte ship A moves along AP while B continues along BC. Our hypothesis is that ship A resumes its original course (and so mov parallel to AC) when it has reached the position P at the sam time as ship B has reached Q, where PQ is parallel to AC. A' subsequent course is along PQ, during which time B is moving along QC. If T is the time needed to resolve the encounter, we have AP = $V_A T$ and BQ = $V_B T$. Projecting on BM (a line draw through B perpendicular to AC) we have

$$BM = BL + LM$$

or
$$b\sin\alpha = V_B\sin\alpha.T + V_A\sin\phi.T$$

giving
$$T = \frac{b\sin\alpha}{V_A\sin\phi + V_B\sin\alpha}. \qquad (7)$$

This result applies, not only to the situation shown in Fig. 5, but also when either of the angles ϕ or α is obtuse.

The mariner will wish to resolve the encounter as quickly as possible, so we are interested in the minimum value of T. Equation (7) shows that this will be attained when $\phi = 90^\circ$, but the minimum is not a sharp one. The further implications of Dr. Kemp's suggestion are still being examined.*

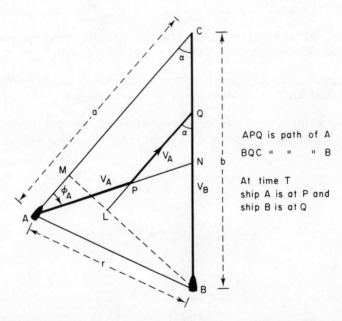

Fig. 5 Resolution of an encounter by action of ship A alone

---

* It was suggested at the Conference that a mariner might well resolve the encounter by turning his ship (A) to face the threat ship (B) and then following B round in a "curve of pursuit" until A had returned to its original heading.

CONCLUSION

This paper has concentrated on a particular mathematical approach to a few specific marine traffic problems. Many other such approaches are possible - e.g. queueing theory, differential game theory or digital simulation - and there is a wide variety of problems to be investigated. It is to be hoped that some of the younger mathematicians will interest themselves in the many new problems that are being posed by the growth and organisation of marine traffic.

REFERENCES

Calvert, E. S. (1960) "Manoeuvres to ensure the avoidance of collision", *J. Inst. Navig.*, **13**, 127.

Calvert, E. S. (1973) "Collision avoidance in a Traffic System" *J. of Navig.*, **26**, 137.

Hall, A. R. and Tilling, L. (*Editors*)(1976) "The Correspondence of Isaac Newton, Vol VI, (1713 - 1718)", C.U.P.

Hollingdale, S. H. (1961) "The Mathematics of Collision Advoidance in two dimensions", *J. Inst. Navig.*, **14**, 243.

Richey, M. (*Editor*) (1970) "Revision of the Collision Regulations: an Interim Report", *J. Inst. Navig.*, **23**, 448.

STATISTICS OF SHIP COLLISIONS

A.N. Cockcroft

(School of Navigation, City of London Polytechnic)

For traffic proceeding in random directions on a plane surface the frequency of collisions, if no avoiding action is taken, is approximately proportional to the square of the traffic density and directly proportional to the size and speed of the craft. Avoiding action is normally taken and the rate of collisions is therefore also governed by additional factors such as the visibility, the effectiveness of the collision-avoidance rules, the competence of personnel, the manoeuvrability of the craft and the efficiency of radar and other equipment.

In the post-war years there has been a considerable increase in the number of merchant ships. The number of vessels of 100 tons gross and upwards increased from less than 30 000 in 1948 to over 65 000 in 1976. When considering the population of ships at risk it is necessary to deduct special types of non-trading vessels and ships laid up. The number of trading ships in service has approximately doubled since 1950 (see Fig. 1) and the greatest increase has been for large ships. The average length of trading ships has increased by approximately 40% in the same period and there has also been an appreciable increase in the mean speed of ships.

Various measures have been taken during the post-war years to improve traffic safety. Radar sets have been fitted to almost all ships, shore systems of surveillance or control have been established and separation schemes have been introduced to separate traffic proceeding in opposite directions. What evidence is there of the effectiveness of these measures?

It is difficult to obtain satisfactory statistics of all ship collisions. This applies especially to collisions occurring in port areas which usually result in only minor damage and are therefore less likely to be reported. World-wide statistics are available from two main sources. Accidents

resulting in the total loss of vessels over 100 tons gross
are reported in the Casualty Returns of Lloyd's Register of
Shipping, with very few exceptions. Collisions occurring outside harbours, rivers and inland waters are unlikely to result
in minor damage and are usually reported in Lloyd's Weekly
Casualty Reports.

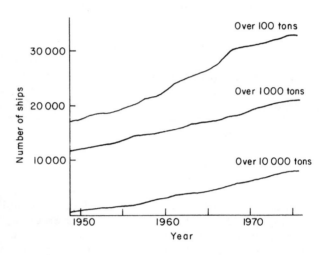

Fig. 1.   Number of trading ships in commission, 1949 to 1976

The incidence of total losses due to collision has increas
by approximately 100% during the last 30 years. There has
been a similar percentage increase of the number of ships in
service so the loss ratio has remained almost constant. The
proportion of ships totally lost by collision at sea, as distin
from losses occurring in harbours, rivers and canals has
remained around 65% during the last 50 years and no clear trend
in this proportion has become apparent.

An investigation of all collisions occurring outside harbours, rivers and inland waters, including both total and parti
losses, has been made for the 20 year period 1957-76. The City
of London Polytechnic computer was used to assist in the analys
of data. Only collisions in which at least one vessel was a
trading ship of over 100 tons gross, and both ships were under
way, were considered.

The total number of sea collisions for the 20 year period
was found to be 2307.   Fig. 2 shows the annual incidence of
all collisions satisfying the above criteria and of collisions

between two trading ships, each of over 1000 tons gross. An analysis of variance on the figures for the four 5 year periods showed no significant time trend, despite the increase in the number and average size of ships at risk.

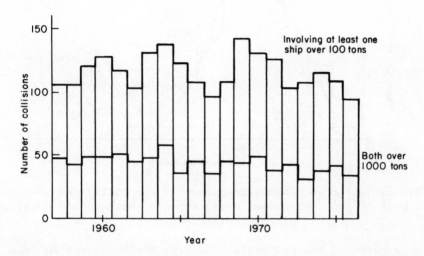

Fig. 2. Annual incidence of sea collisions, 1957 to 1976

A similar lack of significant trend was found by Stratton to apply to different types of air accidents over a 24 year period although there had been a considerable increase in air traffic, aircraft speed and total distance flown. This constancy suggests the possibility that compensating factors tend to be introduced when the number of accidents rises above a certain acceptable level.

Fig. 3 shows the monthly frequency of sea collisions over the 20 year period, together with the expected distribution produced by the Poisson and negative binomial models. The chi-square test gives a good fit for the negative binomial distribution but does not give a good fit for the Poisson. The probability of collision does not remain constant due to such variable factors as visibility.

Nearly 60% of the collisions during the 20 year period occurred off North West Europe, mainly in the southern North Sea and English Channel, but for this region a clear trend

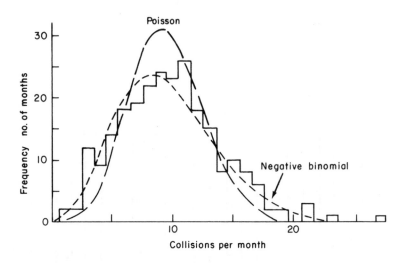

Fig. 3. Observed monthly frequency of sea collisions over the
20 year period compared with the expected Poisson and negative
binomial distributions

was apparent. The proportion off N.W. Europe decreased from
67% of the world total in the first 5 years to 42% in the last
5 years. By contrast, there has been a considerable increase
in the incidence of sea collisions in the coastal regions of
Japan and South East Asia. The increase in Asiatic coastal
waters can be attributed to the increase of traffic density
due to the rapid growth of Japanese trade. Off N.W. Europe
the density of traffic may have decreased slightly but not
sufficiently to account for the improvement in the incidence
of collisions.

    During the first 10 years covered by the survey 467 colli-
sions, approximately 40% of the world total, occurred in the
vicinity of the areas off the coasts of N.W. Europe and N.
America in which traffic separation has now been introduced.
Voluntary traffic separation was first introduced in the Dover
Strait in 1967 and has since been extended to other areas. For
the 5 year period 1972-76 the number of collisions which
occurred in the vicinity of the traffic separation areas was
93, less than 20% of the world total.

Table I

Incidence of collisions in the coastal waters of some major
regions of the world for four 5 year periods since 1957

Region	1957-61	1962-66	1967-71	1972-76	Total 1957-76
N.W. Europe	385	387	316	224	1312
E. Asia inc. Malacca St.	35	67	152	152	406
N. America	60	56	57	33	206
Other regions	95	90	80	118	383
World Total	575	600	605	527	2307

Restricted visibility was reported in just over 35% of
world-wide sea collisions, but the actual proportion is believed
to be appreciably higher as the presence of fog is not always
reported. Approximately 50% of sea collisions were reported
to be in fog off the south and east coasts of the United Kingdom, in the Gibraltar Strait and off the west coast of N.
America. For collisions involving only vessels of over 1000
tons the proportion in restricted visibility decreased from 55%
in the first 5 years to 26% in the last 5 years. The decrease
can be attributed mainly to the effect of traffic separation
but may also be due partly to the increase of traffic density
in regions, such as S.E. Asia, where there is a low incidence
of fog.

The time of collision was reported in 1000 cases, over
60% of the total. When the visibility was reported to be restricted the number occurring in darkness was approximately
the same as in daylight. When the visibility was not reported
the number considered to have occurred in darkness (499) was
twice as great as the number in daylight (248).

Voyage data were available for both ships in 1204 collisions (approximately 80% of collisions between trading ships),
making it possible to deduce the type of encounter. Of this

number 72% were considered to have been meeting or fine crossing encounters, 8% broad crossing, 8% overtaking and the rest
indeterminate.   For sea collisions off N.W. Europe, where the
majority of traffic separation areas have been established,
the proportion of meeting collisions decreased from approximately 80% in the first 10 years to 65% in the last 5 years.
For all other regions the proportion of meeting collisions was
65% over the 20 year period and a chi-square test showed no
significant difference between proportions for the four 5 year
periods.

        Traffic separation was intended to reduce the risk of
collision between vessels proceeding in opposite directions.
In an attempt to isolate the effects of traffic separation
from other effects, such as changes in traffic density, the
numbers of collisions between vessels proceeding in opposite
directions in the vicinity of areas in which traffic separatio
has now been established are compared in Table II over four
5 year periods with the numbers of other types of collision
within those areas and with the numbers of all types of collision occurring outside the separation areas but within the sam
region.   For this purpose the region considered was the Englis
Channel, Dover Strait and southern North Sea.   There has been
a considerable decrease of meeting collisions in the separatio
areas whereas no clear trend is evident for other types of
collision within the region.   Thus it would seem that traffic
separation rather than reduced density is mainly responsible
for the improvement.

                            Table II

Meeting collisions in traffic separation areas compared with
other types of collision within such areas and all types of
collision occurring outside the separation areas, for the
English Channel and southern North Sea, 1957-76.

Type of collision	1957-61	1962-66	1967-71	1972-76
Meeting encounter in TSA	110	102	66	17
Other types of TSA	56	49	62	52
All types outside TSA	46	54	44	45
Total for region	212	205	172	114

Table III shows the number of trading ships in different size categories involved in a sea collision during each of the four 5 year periods since 1957, also the accident ratios obtained by dividing the annual number in collision by the number of ships in service. The ratios are shown to increase with size of ship. There has been a marked improvement in the last 10 years for each size category.

Table III

Numbers of ships in collision with ratios to numbers in service for different size categories, 1957-76

Size Category in gross tons		1957-61	1962-66	1967-71	1972-76
100 to 999	In collision	167	220	223	163
	In service	6900	9300	11000	11500
	Ratio	0.0048	0.0047	0.0040	0.0028
1000 to 9999	In collision	535	525	448	362
	In service	12300	13600	13000	13100
	Ratio	0.0086	0.0078	0.0069	0.0055
10000 & over	In collision	143	222	259	239
	In service	2800	4100	5800	7600
	Ratio	0.0102	0.0108	0.0089	0.0064

The investigation has revealed that although the incidence of collisions has not changed significantly there have been considerable changes in the pattern of accidents. There has been a regional redistribution and a decrease in the proportions occurring in restricted visibility and associated with meeting encounters. Traffic separation is undoubtedly proving to be effective and should result in further improvement now that it has been made compulsory for the ships of all nations to comply with traffic separation schemes.

MATHEMATICAL ASPECTS OF MARINE TRAFFIC CASUALTY STATISTICS

J. R. Moon and J. Higgins

(Liverpool Polytechnic)

INTRODUCTION

Every aspect of human endeavour involves elements of risk
and uncertainty and the shipping industry is no exception.
These may be classified as arising in:

(i) shipping operations, characterised by the probability
of loss due to fluctuating freight rates, not having one's
ship in the right place at the right time, etc.;
(ii) shipping assets, characterised by the probability of
losses due to fluctuating ship prices, both in the new and
second hand market, not buying the ship at the "right" time,
etc.; and
(iii) shipping casualties, characterised by the probability
of financial losses due to the vessel being lost or made non-
operational, cargo losses and personal loss of life or limb
which result from the marine accident.

This paper is concerned with the casualty side of risk
and uncertainty and with the collection, storage and analysis
of marine casualty statistics.

DEFINITION OF A MARINE CASUALTY

Lloyd's Register of Shipping, for the purposes of their
Casualty Returns, identifies four primary causes of an "actual
total loss" of a vessel.

(i) Wrecked - including ships totally lost through stranding,
or striking rocks, sunken wrecks, submerged objects etc.
(ii) Collision - includes ships totally lost through collision with another ship.
(iii) Foundered - includes ships which sank because of the
effects of heavy weather, springing of leaks, etc. This
category also includes vessels posted as Missing or Lost which,

43

for want of sufficient information, or for other reasons, cannot be classified.
(iv) Burnt - including ships destroyed by fire or explosion.

Vessels which are partially lost have similar causes, but
the outcome is not as severe (e.g., the vessel may still be
recovered).

The effects of a marine casualty can also include damage
to personal and third party property (including pollution) and
loss of life and injury to the person.

Thus a marine casualty can be defined as an event (collision, stranding, fire, explosion, etc.) which results in damage to marine property and environment or loss of life or injury to the person.

THE IDEAL CASUALTY FILE

1. Why should casualty statistics be collected?

The short answer is to obtain a better knowledge of our
environment so that more informed decisions can be made.

The three areas of marine activity for which better knowledge is required are insurance, safety and training.

(i) Insurance

One of the objectives of statistical analysis is to shift
an event from the category of uncertainty to that of risk. To
most individual shipowners a marine casualty is an uncertainty.
In aggregate, however, objective or subjective probabilities
can be attached to particular events, this aggregation leading
to certain individuals and companies offering insurance services.
Thus the underwriter can convert the uncertainty into a risk
which in turn becomes a fixed cost to the shipowner in the
form of a premium.

(ii) Safety

It is a truism that absolute safety is unachievable or,
equivalently, absolute safety can only be achieved at infinite
cost. From this point of view the aim of collecting and
analysing accident data is to assist in the identification of
areas where resources need to be allocated in order to improve
safety.

(iii) Training

It appears from both "in-house" and governmental studies (Duclaux (1977) and Taylor (1971)) that approximately 80% of marine accidents are a result of avoidable human errors. However, just as absolute safety is unachievable, so human error in any walk of life cannot be eliminated. The best we can hope to attain is a reduction in the occurrence of these errors. Again however, a resource cost is entailed in training, so it becomes necessary to identify the areas to which such resources should be devoted.

2. What are the causes of a marine casualty?

Given these reasons for collecting casualty statistics and the high speed computers that are at hand, we have to decide upon the data to be stored on file. This can be approached in two ways. First we can suggest hypotheses which need to be tested, and then collect the data to test them. Secondly we can collect all the available data on marine casualties and test the hypotheses later. The appropriate approach lies somewhere between these two, and it is therefore necessary to identify broadly the factors which we believe lead to a marine casualty. As a first step, we select the sub-groups used by Lloyd's in their causes of actual total loss.

Taking the factors which may lead to a collision, we can compile the following list.

1. Merchant Ship Traffic Density - the heavier the traffic density, the greater the probability of meeting another vessel.
2. Fishing Boat Density - similarly the greater the density of fishing boats, the greater the probability of a merchant vessel meeting one.
3. Traffic Separation Schemes - the existence of these schemes will reduce the probability of meeting another vessel in the end-on, or nearly end-on, situation.
4. Weather - the higher the frequency of poor visibility in a particular area, the greater the probability of collision. It may also be expected that an area with a high frequency of gales may have a higher probability of collision because of the associated reduced visibility (due to spray), possible crew exhaustion, reduced manoeuvrability, and reduced radar visibility.
5. Crew Quality - *ceteris-paribus,* it is to be expected that the higher the standard of competence and training of the watchkeeping and perhaps also engineering officers, the less

likely would a collision occur.

6. <u>Crew work load</u> - the greater the work load of the watchkeeping officer, the more likely is his judgement to be impaired
leading to a higher probability of collision. On the other
hand, a low work load may lead to boredom so that the watchkeeping officer becomes less attentive to his duties.

7. <u>Navigational and collision avoidance aids</u> - ideally there
is an optimal level of navigation aids (both in an ergonomic
and an economic sense), so that the closer the vessel's aids
approach this optimum the lower the probability of collision.
These aids, of course, can be double edged, in that even if the
vessel has the optimum level of navigational aids, improper
use can lead to the so called "Radar Assisted Collision" and
the suggested "VHF Assisted Collision". Such aids available
to the watchkeeper will depend upon the size of the ship
(small vessels having less than larger vessels), the age of
the ship (older vessels having less than newer vessels), and
the quality of maintenance (affecting the number of aids available at one time).

8. <u>Reliability of equipment</u> - In a study carried out by one
of our leading shipping companies (Taylor (1971)), equipment
failure was attributed as a cause of one of the collisions.
The failure of steering gear appears to be a major cause.

9. <u>Commercial pressure</u> - the meeting of a schedule, tide or
conditions of a charter-party are all factors which a master
of a ship takes into account, and if allowed to dominate his
regard for International Regulations could have serious con-
sequences.

Considering the other causes of an actual total loss more
briefly we may suggest that the factors leading to a vessel
being <u>wrecked</u> are similar to those of collision, but with a
different emphasis being placed on some of them.

In the case of <u>fire and explosion</u> we have to look towards
different causes.

The major sources of fire on board ships appear to be (Merchant
Shipping "M" Notices, Department of Trade):

1. oil escaping on to hot surfaces;
2. vessels undergoing repairs, particularly welding;
3. spontaneous combustion of cargo and oily rags in bilges,
engine room and stores;
4. static electricity;
5. burning fat in galleys;
6. electrical; and
7. smoking.

The causes of fires, like the sources, tend to be numerous. However the main factors include:

1. crew's adherence to national and international codes of practice for the carriage of goods (e.g., the United Kingdom's "Blue Book", and the IMCO code of practice for the carriage of dangerous goods);
2. crew's adherence to governmental advisory notices concerning the prevention of fire on board ships (e.g., the Department of Trade's Merchant Shipping Notices);
3. crew training in fire prevention;
4. crew training in fire fighting, i.e., even if there is an outbreak of fire an adequately trained crew may be able to contain a fire more effectively;
5. the standards required and maintenance of fire fighting appliances;
6. age of vessel - as the vessel gets older, its wiring will probably deteriorate and so increase the probability of an electrical fire;
7. technological change - with the rapid technological changes of the last decade new problems and causes of fires have emerged. Thus for example there was the loss of three VLCC's from explosion whilst tank washing. The International Chamber of Shipping reported that they were caused by "water slugs" ("Final Report on Explosions in very Large Tankers").
8. Act of God, e.g., vessel struck by lightning.

Finally, in the case of foundering we can identify the following factors as causes:

1. size of vessel - the smaller the vessel, the greater the possibility of being overwhelmed in heavy weather;
2. age of vessel - the older the vessel, the greater the probability of its structure failing or leaking;
3. the area where the vessel trades - the greater the percentage of its time which a vessel spends in an area where heavy weather is expected, the greater the probability of loss;
4. technological change - today when we are constantly at the threshold of technology, new design techniques and steels are being used which have not had the test of time;
5. cargo carried - any cargo which is not securely stowed, lashed and shored is liable to shift in heavy weather. There are also certain other classes of cargo which are inherently unstable and are liable to shift unless adequate precautions are taken to prevent it;
6. distribution of cargo within the vessel - cargo should be stowed so as not to unduly stress the vessel, as heavy weather

could compound these inherent stresses.

3. What statistics should we collect?

    Given the major factors which contribute to a marine
casualty, we ideally require data on each cause. Taking collision as an example, we would need to know the merchant ship
and fishing boat density,proximity to the coastline, and whether
a traffic separation scheme was available at the time of the
casualty. We should also need to know the navigational aids
being used, the weather conditions, and full details of the
competency, training and perception of the watchkeeping officer
prior to the casualty occurring. Unfortunately, however, these
data are not always available and we have to resort to averages
and proxies for these factors. Thus continuing the collision
example, we could use average traffic density figures and
average weather conditions for the area under consideration.
If information is not available on the navigational aids actually being used, we may use the proxy of navigational aids
fitted to the vessel. Finally, if we accept that 80% of marine
casualties are due to "errors in judgement", then it is this
human element which is of utmost importance. Regrettably international data on the competency and training of crews are not
available, and it is here that the most contentious proxies
have to be used. "Where else can this be sought except under
Flag (registration)?" (Beer (1969)). Two further proxies for
the quality of crew are size of vessel, where one may hypothesise that the shipowner cannot afford not to employ a well
trained and competent crew on a large vessel; and age of vessel,
where one may hypothesise that it is the "people who are very
anxious to speculate, very anxious to come into the world of
trade (and) very anxious to start a growth industry" (Telfer
in Beer (1969)) who purchase old vessels.

4. Where do we collect the statistics?

    (i) The ideal primary source of data would be from a full
scale investigation of each case. Unfortunately even if the
investigation was "without prejudice" and resources were available to undertake the exercise, the key interviewees may have
been lost, or the way in which they perceived the casualty may
be incorrect.
    (ii) Data could be extracted from published court cases.
This is an invaluable source of information for individual
cases but only a very small percentage of the total casualties
are actually reported.

(iii)   Data could be sifted from the full reports by the assured
to his insurer.   This information is confidential to the insurer
and it must therefore be left to him to publish the salient
features.
  (iv)   There are the reports in the shipping press (for example
Lloyd's List).
  (v)   The insurance societies' returns give summary details
of casualties.

        In the event the sources used, however, depend on the
information and financial resources available to the collecting
agency.

LIVERPOOL POLYTECHNIC'S MARINE CASUALTY FILE

        The Marine Casualty Data File at Liverpool Polytechnic's
Department of Maritime Studies was commenced in June 1972 with
the cooperation of the Liverpool Underwriters' Association.
The file contains all the casualties reported by the Association
in their Monthly Casualty Returns since the beginning of 1969.
In addition, details of the vessels involved in the casualty
are supplemented by data contained in Lloyd's Register of
Shipping.   In particular, the data contained in each of these
sources are as follows:

L.U.A. Monthly Returns

1.   Date of casualty.
2.   Name of ship.
3.   Port of Registry.
4.   Flag.
5.   Gross tonnage.
6.   Year of build.
7.   Owners.
8.   Route
9.   Cargo.
10. Casualty type.
11. Position.
12. Particulars, for example: (i) whether in fog;
                                (ii) loss of life.
13. Whether partial loss, total loss, constructive total loss,
or partial loss later declared a constructive total loss.

Lloyd's Register

14. Type of vessel.
15. Classification Society.
16. Navigational aids:

     (i) Direction finder.
    (ii) Echo-sounder.
  (iii) Gyro-compass.
   (iv) Position finding device.
    (v) Radar.
   (vi) Radio telephone.
17. Engine type.
18. Engine power.
19. Managers.
20. Deadweight.

These data are coded on to a standard form designed for eight
(80 character) punch cards. These cards are divided as follows

1 and 2	Vessel data.
3 and 4	Voyage data.
5	Casualty data.
6, 7 and 8	Damage and Information.

STORAGE AND RETRIEVAL OF DATA

    Storage and retrieval of data are achieved by means of
COBAL programs which are contained in a program library, and
the ICL computer packages "FIND-2 Multiple Enquiry System" and
"Direct Access Sorting". Five types of COBOL program are used:

  (i)   to describe and establish storage space on magnetic
       tape;
 (ii)   to output contents of the casualty file to line printer;
(iii)   to validate data on the magnetic tape;
 (iv)   to amend and update the casualty file;
  (v)   to search the data fields according to the users require
       ments.

With the introduction of the two ICL packages, the COBOL
search programs have become more or less redundant. The data
for the analysis in this paper were retrieved in the following
manner:

1. The age of the vessel at the time of the incident was
found using a COBOL program and stored with each record.
2. The "Direct Access Sorting" package sorted the data according to flag.
3. FIND-2 was used to produce two way tables of AGE-TYPE or
AGE-SIZE by flag.

ANALYSES USING THE CASUALTY FILE

1. Introduction

The central problem in the interpretation of accident statistics arises from the multiplicity of factors that may be adduced as contributory causes. At one extreme, a total or partial loss classified by age, type and size of ship involved, by cargo type and time of accident renders the situation unique and no statistical techniques are available to interpret the incident. At the other extreme, all accidents occurring in a given time period may be considered as a single group and while this may enable statistical comparisons to be made between one period and another there is a danger that such analyses produce misleading conclusions due to aggregating possibly heterogeneous data.

Much work has been published on the analysis of marine accident figures including the masterly summaries of Cashman (1977), Beer (1969), and, for example, the OECD reports (1972). Generally, though many of the publications present cross-classified data, comments and inferences have mainly been restricted to describing and comparing the relative risks in the sub-categories of a single factor such as age or size.

One of the first uses to which Liverpool Polytechnic's Marine Casualty File has been put was to generate data to give insight:

(i) into the extent to which conclusions drawn from a one-way classification of a single factor need to be modified when other factors are taken into account;
(ii) to assess the relative importance of the various factors in explaining accident rates.

Two such analyses are considered here – one using AGE-FLAG-TYPE (of ship), the other using the AGE-FLAG-SIZE factors. In both cases the File was searched for the numbers of total and partial losses recorded for the years 1969-1975 inclusive. These data were supplemented by the total number of ship-years at risk (in the categories used) from Lloyd's Registers of Shipping. Insofar as the polytechnic file does not contain all casualties and that no adjustments have been made to the "at risk" figures for vessels laid up, etc., the actual percentage of incidents in the sub-categories may be biased; but as the investigation is concerned with the changes in the sizes of the effects produced by the insertion of other factors, any such biases

are not likely to affect the conclusions. Similarly as the
effects determined are used to predict only the future patterns
of accidents in the Liverpool Underwriters cases, the biases
only reflect that Association's particular "portfolio". One
of the major problems in casualty statistics is the comparison
of like with like. Two methods which may be used are, first,
to express the losses in each cell as a percentage of the total
number of vessels at risk in that cell. Second, one may choose
a reference flag and convert the losses of all other flags in
terms of the standard (i.e. we are asking the question what
would the losses of other flags be if they had the same structure as the standard). Both of these methods have their
idiosyncrasies, particularly when the number of vessels at risk
in a cell is small. The following analyses therefore employ
the standard statistical method of handling such problems,
the GLIM Statistical Computer Package (Nelder (1975)) being
used as an aid to computation. In this method the rate of
loss figures are analysed as Binomial proportions in three-way
contingency tables assuming linear effects on the LOGIT scale.
If p is the proportion of incidents to ships at risk, then
for the first model

$$\ln[p/(1-p)] = GM + AGE + FLAG + TYPE$$

where GM: general mean level,
     AGE: a set of numbers depending only on the age of the
          ship at the time of accident,
    FLAG: a set of numbers representing the general effect on
          the accident rate of various flags of registration,
    TYPE: a set of numbers representing the different risks
          associated with the different types of ship.
Similarly for the second model

$$\ln[p/(1-p)] = GM + AGE + FLAG + SIZE$$

where SIZE: a set of figures measuring the effect of the gross
          tonnage of the ship on accident rate.
Four analyses were carried out on each of the two data sets
comprising:

 (i)   the three marginal analyses taking each factor separately
(ii)   a joint analysis including the main effects of all three
factors.

2. Model I: AGE-FLAG-TYPE

The file produced 1328 incidents out of 99 231 ship-years
at risk leading to an over-all crude incident rate of 1.34%.
Tables I, II and III contrast the magnitudes of the effects in

TABLE I

	AGE (yrs)	0-4	5-9	10-14	15-19	20-24	25 and over
% Incident	MARGINAL	0.756	0.973	1.316	2.133	2.244	2.271
	MAIN	0.764	1.004	1.241	1.812	1.865	1.905

TABLE II

	FLAG*	UK	FR	WG	GR	IT	JA	LI	NO	SW
% Incident	MARGINAL	1.454	0.675	0.770	2.740	1.082	0.485	2.300	1.092	1.094
	MAIN	1.753	0.832	1.088	2.761	1.110	0.696	2.273	1.341	1.364

United Kingdom (UK), France (FR), West Germany (WG), Greece (GR), Italy (IT), Japan (JA), Liberia (LI), Norway (NO), Sweden (SW).

* These produced mainly non-zero entries in the numbers at risk.

C

the MARGINAL (one factor at a time) and MAIN (all three factc
together) models.

TABLE III

	TYPE	TANKER	BULK/ORE	OTHER*
% Incident	MARGINAL	1.485	1.671	1.212
	MAIN	1.289	1.700	1.133

* (dry cargo, fishing, etc.)

It is noticeable in Table I that after an initial rapid
increase of risk with age group, the values level out in the
last three cells. This is true for both analyses but the MAI
model values are less for the older ships than are the MARGIN
figues; the implication being that the different flags have
fleets of differing age composition.

Table II shows that although the rank order of risk is
virtually identical for the two models, the MAIN effects allow
ing as they do for age and type of ship are generally higher
than the MARGINAL values.

The differences between the TYPE categories are shown in
Table III - partially hidden in the MARGINAL analysis by the
age profiles of the different flags, with greater differences
showing up in the MAIN figures.

As far as predictability is concerned, 72% of the variability in the data is accounted for by a knowledge of the AGE,
FLAG and TYPE category of the ship concerned and taking the
range of risk values as a measure of importance, the categori
run in the order FLAG (0.696 to 2.761%), AGE (0.764 to 1.905%
and then TYPE (1.133 to 1.700%).

3. *Model II: AGE-FLAG-SIZE*

In order to keep the size of the problem within the limit
tions of the polytechnic's computer and to investigate variou
flag effects, Sweden and Italy were omitted and Cyprus (CY),
Panama (PA) and the Phillipines (PH) were included. The
results are shown in Tables, IV, V and VI. The AGE groups
were those used in the first analysis and the SIZE groups
(in gross tons) were as shown in Table VI.

TABLE IV

AGE (years)	0-4	5-9	10-14	15-19	20-24	25 and over
% Incident MARGINAL	0.741	1.008	1.457	2.476	2.748	2.858
MAIN	0.982	1.343	1.625	2.229	2.365	2.137

TABLE V

FLAG	UK	CY	FR	WG	GR	JA	LI	NO	PA	PH
% Incident MARGINAL	1.401	4.648	0.679	0.747	2.635	0.475	2.253	1.080	3.024	3.331
MAIN	1.560	3.935	0.771	0.932	2.527	0.626	2.535	1.308	2.814	3.026

TABLE VI

Size	500-999	1000-1999	2000-5999	6000-9999	10 000-19 999	20 000 and over
% Incident MARGINAL	1.262	1.650	1.714	1.777	1.849	1.196
MAIN	1.607	1.759	1.640	1.565	1.684	1.426

The over-all crude incident rate is 1.548%,which is high
than the corresponding rate in the first analysis and reflect
the change in the flags considered.

In Table IV the age effects in the MAIN model are less
extreme than those in the MARGINAL row, i.e. when AGE and FLA
are duly allowed for, the change in rate with age is considerably reduced. It is disturbing to note that the MAIN effects
in Table IV are considerably higher than those in Table I,
i.e. the AGE values are affected by the introduction/absence
of SIZE and TYPE categories.

After accounting for age and size, the FLAG differences
are smaller in the MAIN analysis of Table V as compared with
the MARGINAL values (i.e. the range of parameter values are
greater in the marginal analysis than in the main analysis),
although it is comforting here that the entries for the MAIN
effects in the countries common to the two analyses (in Table
II and IV) are very similar.

The SIZE categories in Table VI do not show any simple
pattern. In the MARGINAL case there is an increase in risk
up to the final category,whereas in the MAIN model there is a
suggestion of a decrease. A knowledge of the AGE, FLAG and
SIZE of a ship accounted for 64% of the variability of this
data set and the range of risk values puts the categories
in order of importance as FLAG (0.626 to 3.935%), AGE (0.982
to 2.365%) and SIZE (1.426 to 1.759%).

4. *Model Stability*

In order to assess how effective predictions made by the
model could be, the ships at risk figures were collected for
1976 and the numbers of the incidents predicted from the MAIN
model in Analysis I. The numbers of accidents recorded on
file for 1976 were produced and the observed and predicted
numbers are shown in Table VII. (In order to again produce
mainly non-zero entries the three way analysis has been
collapsed into a 4x4 two way table).

The total number of incidents observed for 1976 is less
(19%) than those predicted from the MAIN model using the 1976
at risk figures. However, there is some relationship between
the two sets of figures in that the rank correlation of the
predicted with the observed is 0.65.

TABLE VII

Numbers of Incidents - 1976

AGE (years)	0-4	5-9	10-14	15 and over	TOTALS
FLAG FR, JA	3	12	9	3	27
	(4.6)	(8.0)	(4.9)	(5.6)	(23.1)
WG, IT	1	1	3	5	10
	(2.2)	(4.0)	(2.9)	(8.7)	(17.8)
NO, SW, UK	8	3	4	6	21
	(9.0)	(10.7)	(8.3)	(17.2)	(45.2)
LI, GR	10	16	12	73	111
	(16.1)	(19.6)	(19.2)	(67.7)	(122.6)
TOTALS	22	32	28	87	169
	(31.9)	(42.3)	(35.3)	(99.2)	(208.7)

Unbracketed values are observed and bracketed values are predicted.

SUMMARY AND CONCLUSIONS

1. Three of the questions which were asked in this paper concerned the causes of a marine casualty, the required statistics and their sources. Whilst a list of causes were presented, it was suggested (i) that precise data on every casualty may be extremely difficult to obtain and will depend upon the resources available to the collecting agency, and (ii) that all accidents occurring in a given time period may be considered as a single group. However, the unique nature of a casualty and the problems of aggregating heterogeneous data must be borne in mind in any subsequent analysis.
2. In this exploratory analysis, two models examining AGE-FLAG-TYPE and AGE-FLAG-SIZE of vessel have been considered. From the TYPE analysis, it can be stated in general terms that the MAIN model reduces the AGE effect for older vessels, increases the FLAG effect and reduces the TYPE effect for tankers and others. The relationships in the SIZE analysis tend to be more complicated. However, we can draw two significant conclusions from both models.

1. There are differences between the MAIN and MARGINAL
    models, thus indicating the necessity for considerin
    more than one factor at a time.
2. The differing size of the AGE category effects in
    the two models is indicative that at least a four
    way analysis (FLAG, AGE, TYPE and SIZE) is necessary
    to produce a more realistic evaluation of the data.
3. In view of the elementary model used, the agreement betwe
predicted and actual incidents is heartening in that, without
a detailed knowledge of the individual ships involved, reason
able forecasts of the numbers of accidents in various categor
can be made.
4. Finally, the answer to the original question (why should
casualty statistics be collected?) lies in obtaining better
knowledge for marine insurance, safety and training. The met
of analysis has shown how a casualty file can be of assistanc

(i)   To the underwriter and broker; a knowledge of the
FLAG, AGE and SIZE of vessel accounts for 64%, and a knowledg
of FLAG, AGE and TYPE of vessel accounts for 72% of the variability in the data (the importance of each factor being in
that order);
(ii)   To those concerned with safety on an international
scale FLAG and AGE of the vessels in the fleet are of major
importance; on a domestic scale, AGE is of major importance;
(iii)   To those concerned with training - whilst this paper
does not indicate specific areas where more resources should
be devoted it does suggest, *ceterus paribus*, a substantial
difference between the casualty rates of various FLAGS.

REFERENCES

Beer, W. J., "Analysis of World Merchant Ship Losses", *Trans
R.I.N.A.* January 1969.

Cashman, J. D., "Analysis of World Merchant Ship Losses
1967-1975", Second West European Conference on Marine Technol
London, May 1977.

I.C.L., "FIND-2 Multiple Enquiry System", I.C.L. London. 1977

I.C.L., "Direct Access Sorting", I.C.L. London. 1975

International Chamber of Shipping, "Final Report on Explosion
in Very Large Tankers".

Nelder, J. A., "General Linear Interactive Modelling", Numerical Algorithms Group, Oxford. NAGLIM:G55/G33:Re12:Aug 75.

O.E.C.D., "Marine Transport 1972".

Taylor, R. J. F., "The Shipping Revolution and trying to learn from it", The 40th Andrew Laing Lecture 1971.

Xavier Duclaux, "Why Unsafety at Sea", Second West European Conference on Marine Technology, London, May 1977.

MARINE TRAFFIC SURVEY METHODS: DATA COLLECTION AND PROCESSING

J. Kemp and J. Holmes

(Marine Traffic Research Unit, City of London Polytechnic)

INTRODUCTION

As we understand it, there are two main aims in this Conference:

(1) to introduce navigators to the idea that mathematical methods can contribute usefully to the solution of marine traffic problems;

(2) to arouse the interest of uncommitted mathematicians in some of the problems which arise in marine traffic studies.

In this paper we shall concentrate on the second of these objectives. Section 1 (J.K.) discusses data collection and Section 2 (J.H.) discusses some aspects of data processing. What we say about data collection will probably sound self-evident to those already in the field, but the approach will be justified if it helps to interest a few uncommitted people in the systematic study of marine traffic problems.

SECTION 1. DATA COLLECTION (J.K.)

1. Data Sources

There are three main sources of data for the investigation of marine traffic problems, i.e., questionnaire techniques, the use of simulators, and the observation of marine traffic behaviour in the field. Each source has its advantages and disadvantages which can be briefly noted as follows.

(i) Questionnaire techniques are valuable for acquiring factual data such as what equipment is carried aboard a sample of ships. They can be useful for obtaining opinions from experienced personnel so that problem areas may be identified which require special study. They are unreliable for purposes such as assessing the probable behaviour of ships in hypothetical

61

situations, where subjects are asked what their reactions would
be to some imaginary scenarios.

(ii)   The use of simulators gives the possibility of perfectl
controlled experiments which can be replicated for a number
of subjects and where the variables can be injected and measured with considerable precision. There is always some arti-
ficiality and some lack of input compared with the real life
situation and possibly some additional input which is not present in the real life situation.

(iii) Observation of marine traffic behaviour in the field
provides completely authentic data but the method of collection gives rise to some errors, and the data collected are
usually incomplete in certain respects. Also, the independent
variables which may be affecting traffic cannot be controlled
and it may not be possible to measure all of the dependent
variables which may be of interest.

A more detailed discussion of the advantages and disadvantages of these data sources has been presented elsewhere,
but no one method is sufficient in itself for a reasonably
complete study of traffic in a particular area. Here we shall
concentrate on the third method, i.e., real life traffic surveys, and consider further some of the data collection problem
associated with this method.

2. *Visual Survey Methods*

Visual observation of ships has the advantage of simplicity and is particularly useful for the measurement of traffi
passing along a relatively narrow waterway. Individual ships
may often be positively identified by name as well as by class
and the method is particularly suitable for ascertaining the
number of ships crossing a given datum line across the waterway. Resolution is excellent, so that even very small craft
may be readily observed and it is possible to separate individual craft amongst a number which may be navigating in close
company. Disadvantages of the method are that range is difficult to measure so that the distribution of ships across a
waterway is not easy to ascertain. For similar reasons the
speed distribution of ships using the waterway is difficult
to derive unless observations are made as the ships pass over
two separate datum lines a known distance apart. A further
limitation of the method is that identification of individual
ships is not usually possible at night and that the method

fails altogether in fog conditions, heavy rain, etc. when
observations may be of particular interest. Visual surveys
have been used very extensively and successfully in Japan
where the geography is well suited to this method. At City
of London Polytechnic we have used visual methods mainly as a
back-up to radar surveys.

3. Radar Traffic Survey Methods

Radar has many advantages as a primary means of collecting traffic survey data. It fixes the position of ships in
the coverage area in two dimensions so that the distribution
of ships over the area may be ascertained and, by comparing
the instantaneous positions of individual ships at different
times, velocities may be easily deduced. Radar operates by
day and by night and is reasonably independent of weather
conditions.

A disadvantage is that radar, of itself, does not identify individual ships, even by class. Also, there are limitations of range and resolution. Using standard 3 cm marine
radar equipment on the Polytechnic training/survey vessel
"Sir John Cass", it has been found that there is little difficulty in identifying reliable echoes from ships of 500 gross
registered tons (g.r.t.) or more at a range of 10 miles. For
small ships, however, the range at which reliable echoes may
be obtained decreases and, in some conditions, small wooden
fishing vessels or fibre glass yachts may not be detected at
all. This is particularly the case where sea clutter or other
interference is present on the plan position indicator (P.P.I).
For simple counts of the number of ships over a given size
using a particular area, it may not be necessary to detect
the smaller craft but, if the behaviour of the larger ships
is of interest, then a knowledge of the presence of the smaller
ships is necessary insofar as this may affect the manoeuvring
patterns of the larger ones.

The theoretical resolution with which it is possible to
distinguish between adjacent target ships depends mainly on
the pulse length for ships on the same bearing and mainly on
beam width for two ships at the same range. Reduction in
range clearly gives better discrimination between adjacent
ships at the same range for a given beam width. Reduction in
range also gives the possibility of better discrimination between adjacent ships on the same bearing since reliable echoes
may be obtained using a shorter pulse length.

In summary, it may be suggested that a 24 mile range
scale is unsatisfactory for surveys by ship-borne radars because the radar horizon is much less than this for any reasonable height of scanner. Shore-based radars such as are used
to cover the Dover Strait can be sited at adequate heights
and larger scanners can also be used to reduce the beam width.

The 12 mile range scale is likely to give reliable information on ships of 2000 g.r.t. and upwards, with a resolution of the order of 0.1 mile. This is sufficient, not only
to give information on the distribution of ships over the survey area, but also an indication of the interactions which
take place between individual ships.

The 6 mile and 3 mile range scales provide increased
resolution and more reliable acquisition of small targets, and
for the detailed investigation of ship movements in channels,
it may be necessary to use 1½ or ¾ mile range scales. As the
scale of the radar picture is increased, the trade-off is
clearly between the better resolution and acquisition of small
targets on the one hand, and the reduction in coverage area
and concomitant reduction in size of traffic sample on the
other.

4. *Methods of Recording Survey Data*

(i) Direct plotting from a radar P.P.I. is a useful method
of recording data when traffic densities are low and sufficien
manpower is available at the survey station. The real time
plot of ship movements can be maintained on transparent sheets
placed over a reflection plotter on the radar display itself,
or by the transfer of ranges and bearings from the P.P.I. to
a separate plotting table. Direct plotting has the advantage
that less processing is subsequently required and also that
ambiguities and tracking problems which arise when ships pass
near each other can be identified and resolved as they arise.
It has been used by City of London Polytechnic researchers,
particularly for the detailed investigation of traffic pattern
in channels where, as explained in the previous section, it
was necessary to study small areas on a large scale (e.g., the
1½ mile range scale) and hence relatively few ships at a time,
in order to achieve the required high resolution. Visual
methods were employed concurrently to give back-up data which
could be used to resolve plotting problems as they occurred
and to identify, at least by class, the ships observed on the
radar. This method has been used by the Netherlands Pilots
Association for collecting data off the Hook of Holland.

(ii) Photography of the P.P.I. is a method which is capable
of dealing with larger concentrations of traffic than direct
plotting. For observing traffic flows and interactions in
coastal waters we have found that a 3 minute interval between
successive photographs of the P.P.I. is a reasonable compromise
between the need for good data and the need to economise on
films and the time needed for subsequent data extraction. An
advantage of the method is that each photograph fixes the relative positions of all the ships in the survey area instant-
aneously, whereas in the direct plotting method the targets
have to be marked on the plot sequentially so that successive
target points are not all related to the same instant of time.
In order to allow for small targets which do not paint at
every sweep, and also to increase the brightness of all the
targets relative to the interference, we have found that an
exposure time equivalent to 3 sweeps provides satisfactory
results. A disadvantage of the method is that further processing is necessary in order to recast the recorded data
into a form suitable for study and interpretation, for instance
by constructing plots or by extracting the positions of ships
in cartesian coordinates for subsequent computer analysis.
This is a method which has been used extensively at the City
of London Polytechnic, but again it is felt necessary to keep
a visual lookout going simultaneously in order to provide
checking and back-up information. Photography of the P.P.I.
is also the standard form in which data are collected by the
Coast Guard Station at St. Margaret's Bay, although the time
interval used there is 1 minute instead of 3 minutes.

(iii) The direct feed of radar information to a computer has
the advantage that very large quantities of data can be handled
economically. It suffers from the same limitations as all
methods based on radar performances and so needs to be backed
up by information from other sources, (e.g., for identification
of ships by class) which tends to reduce its economic advantage. Also, there are considerable tracking problems when
ships pass close to each other, particularly if they manoeuvre
at the same time. The programming problems which have to be
overcome in order to provide a reliable output are considerable.
This approach has been used by the Royal Dutch Shell Labora-
tories/Netherlands Maritime Institute investigation of marine
traffic flows in the Hook of Holland Roads.

5. *Siting of Survey Stations*

Shore sites are generally the most convenient, but suffer
from the disadvantage that they are often remote from the

traffic to be observed. They are particularly suitable for
the survey of traffic using narrow waterways near shore, but
are less suitable for observing offshore areas. When radar
is used, the remoteness of the area to be surveyed may to
some extent be compensated for by choosing an elevated site
and a larger scanner (and hence a narrower beam width) than
is practicable with ship-borne equipment. An off-centred
display allows a reasonable scale to be used for the display.
Despite these measures, lack of discrimination and loss of
poorly reflecting targets remains a problem.

Stationary shipborne survey stations have the advantage
that they can work much closer to the survey area and hence
acquire both better visual and radar information. They are
generally expensive to operate but they can, of course, be
easily deployed to cover different areas as required. Particularly when studying detailed traffic movements in small
areas, it must always be borne in mind that the presence of
the survey vessel itself may have some disturbing influence
on the behaviour of the shipping under observation. City of
London Polytechnic practice has been to anchor the survey
ship in a recognised anchorage where other ships are frequentl
to be found so that the presence of the survey ship is part
of the normal shipping pattern in the area. The radar display
may be off-centred to cover the survey area on a suitable rang
scale.

Moving ship-borne survey stations can be used but it is
not easy to take the survey ship's movements out of the relative movement of other ships in the area so that their true
movement can be derived. This is particularly so if the survey ship does not move at constant velocity. Some interesting data collection using this method has been carried out by
the German Shipowner's Association in collaboration with Ham-
burg University. The method used has been to photograph the
P.P.I. of vessels on regular commercial shipping voyages,
using an automatic 8 millimetre camera. This gives a continuous record of the distribution of other ships around the survey ship and some interesting analyses of these records have
been carried out. There are, however, many limitations in
the data acquired in this way, although the method itself is
very economical

6. *Summary*

The purpose of this section has been to discuss some of
the available marine traffic survey methods. Each has its
limitations and these are reflected in the limitations of the
data derived from them. The analysis applied to the data is

very much the business of the mathematician and statistician
and they must have due concern for the inaccuracies and incom-
pleteness of the raw material with which they must, perforce,
work. The many uncontrolled variables which may affect real
life data constitute an additional difficulty.

SECTION 2. DATA PROCESSING (J.H.)

    This section considers basic methods of organising and
processing marine traffic survey data. In conclusion my
experience in using a variety of standard statistical packages
to analyse the data is considered. The discussion is confined
to general points and no specific results of particular investigations are given.

7. *Data Organisation and Processing*

    The fundamental information which is usually required
from a marine traffic survey is the position of all ships in
an area at a given time in a defined coordinate system, repeated
at regular time intervals, together with identification details
on the ships. For many purposes it is also useful to record
the speed and direction of movement of each ship at each time
point. The choice of time interval will depend on many
factors such as the density of traffic, the size of area being
covered, the sophistication of the recording equipment and
the purpose of the investigation.

    In some recent surveys conducted in the Hook of Holland
Roads by the Netherlands Maritime Institute, a Digiplot with
a 15 second time interval was used, whereas for work undertaken
by the Marine Traffic Research Unit at the City of London
Polytechnic off Harwich, a 6 minute time interval was considered most suitable.

    Examples of data processing used for some of those sur-
veys conducted off Harwich are described.

    The marine traffic surveys were carried out on board the
M.V. "Sir John Cass", the research vessel of the School of
Navigation at the City of London Polytechnic. The area in
which the surveys were conducted was in the North Sea, about
12 miles from Harwich and centred on the Sunk lightvessel.
The area covers an intersection of routes from East Coast ports
to North-West Europe and the English Channel, and thus has a
high traffic density. The basic method used in the surveys

was to plot the positions of all ships in the area every 6
minutes from a marine radar display equipped with a reflection
plotter, on to a roll of transparent film attached. During
each survey the "Sir John Cass" was at anchor and notes were
kept of all ships observed in the area. Identification of
many of the vessels was made possible at a later stage with
the help of the Harwich pilot station.

     The position of a ship at any time was required in
Cartesian coordinates. The origin was the position of the
"Sir John Cass", and the direction of the positive y-axis
was along the North line from there. A transparent grid could
then be placed over the plots and the positions of ships at
a particular time read off. Each ship observed during a survey was given a unique identification number, indicating the
particular survey and the number of the ship.

     The format of the computer records of the surveys were
such that each ship at each time was treated as a separate
record. The information on each record, corresponding to one
card, was as follows:

Ship number   ⎫
Length of ship   ⎪   one record
Gross tonnage of ship   ⎬   per ship
Maximum speed of ship   ⎭

Ship number   ⎫
X coordinate of position at time T   ⎪   successive records
Y coordinate of position at time T   ⎬   of ship's position
Time T   ⎪   in the area
Position in the area   ⎭

     The coordinates measuring the position were recorded to
the nearest tenth of a nautical mile since this was felt to
be the highest degree of accuracy justified. The time T was
read in as an actual value such as 1524, and not in the form
of time points from the start of the survey. The variable,
position in the area, was used to distinguish between ships
in different parts of the area where the navigating conditions
might be altered, such as within 1 nautical mile of the pilot
boat.

     The length of a ship between perpendiculars (in feet),
the gross registered tonnage and the maximum speed could be

found in Lloyd's Register of Shipping whenever a ship had been identified. Special code numbers were entered when the type of ship alone could be identified.

The speed of a ship at any time point T could be calculated easily by evaluating the change in X and Y coordinates between time T - 1 and T. Other quantities of interest could be calculated by writing or adapting simple computer programs for use with the above data records.

An alternative method of data organisation would be by time point rather than by ship number. However, if there were a large amount of data the speed of each ship at time T becomes difficult to calculate since a search for each ship's record at time T - 1 would not always be possible. One method of overcoming this could be to include on the data record for each ship at time T its position at time T - 1.

The main emphasis in the data processing was to perform the tasks required, not to perform them in the most efficient way possible. The methods described are therefore presented as ones which have worked for the research I have undertaken.

Looking critically at the data, there is the problem of loss of radar targets as the distance from the centre of the radar screen increases. There will inevitably be a falling off in data at greater distances from the centre, a problem common to all types of survey by radar. In addition there are problems of sea clutter around the centre of the screen and false and multiple echoes.

8. Selection of Variables

The object of the marine traffic study with which I am involved is to examine statistically the effect of various factors on the time or distance separation from another ship at which a navigator makes a collision avoidance manoeuvre.

The independent X-variables chosen for the study and subsequently investigated were as follows:

1. Position in the area(coded)
2. Number of other (potentially) threatening ships in the area
3. Gross tonnage of central ship
4. Length of central ship

5. Maximum speed of central ship
6. Speed of central ship at time of first decision   (TFD)
7. Speed of most threatening ship at TFD
8. Relative bearing of most threatening ship at TFD
9. Time of most threatening ship to intersection of courses
    at TFD.

    The dependent Y-variables chosen for the study were as
follows:

1. Distance of central ship from most threatening ship at
    TFD,
2. Distance of central ship from intersection of courses
    with most threatening ship at TFD,
3. Time of central ship to intersection of courses with most
    threatening ship at TFD,
4. Indirect distance of central ship from most threatening
    ship at TFD (i.e. distance apart via the point of inter-
    section of courses),
5. Distance of central ship from domain boundary of most
    threatening ship at TFD,
6. Time of central ship to domain boundary at TFD,
7. Type of manoeuvre undertaken by central ship's navigator
    at TFD (coded by change in course and/or speed).

    For some of the data, the distance, time and bearing
variables were measured by hand directly from the plots,
rather than by writing a computer program to perform the task.
The problems with such as program are that it would have to
recognise a "significant" manoeuvre as well as pinpoint the
most threatening ship at any given time point.

9. Use of Statistical Packages

    It was intended that the dependent variables be consid-
ered separately, with the effects of the independent variables
on each of them being evaluated. In the first instance it
was decided that a multiple regression and correlation analysis should be carried out for each dependent variable on all
of the independent variables. For this purpose the Statistical
Package for the Social Sciences (SPSS) subprogram REGRESSION,
and Biomedical Data Package (BMD) program BMDO2R, were found
to be equally suitable.

    The inter-correlations between the X and Y variables
were of inital interest in pinpointing high correlations.

A stepwise (step-up) regression analysis indicates the relative importance of each of the independent variables in contributing to the total variance of the dependent variable used in the model. One can also directly compare the results for each of the dependent variables with a view to deciding which of them is best explained by a set of significant independent variables for the particular set of data collected.

A direct examination of residuals, involving a search for visible patterns, is also of use, where the residuals are plotted against the predicted Y values. Violations of underlying assumptions concerning the error component are indicated by "abnormalities" in the scatter plot, which roughly means a non-straight band pattern.

The SPSS and BMD programs mentioned both offer these and other facilities and have been found to be particularly convenient to use in analysing the marine traffic survey data I have collected so far. Follow-up procedures may involve the use of other statistical packages since one may wish to carry out a discriminant analysis between groups of data, or a factor analysis using any combination of variables.

One must be careful in interpreting the output from statistical packages. Familiarity with the statistical methods being used is essential as one usually needs to weed out the useful (primary) output from the secondary output. The particular packages referred to are well documented, although the actual routines used are rarely listed as part of the documentation.

3.   CONCLUSION

In conclusion it can be seen that Marine Traffic Survey data can be processed automatically and hence quickly. Much work is going on at present in various institutions on methods of collecting data, and it is clear that there will be more advances in the future.

It can also be see   that standard statistical packages may be used for analysing marine traffic data.

THE UNDERWATER ENVIRONMENT:

CHARTING THE SEA BED

R. L. Cloet

(University of Bath)

Ports have developed in waters which were in greater
or lesser degree naturally sheltered from intense wave
activity and excessive flow. This protection has in many
cases been provided by barriers, such as sandbanks, which
are capable of absorbing the energies of wave and flow.
However, in absorbing these high energies, the barriers themselves undergo a degree of instability, and the extent of
horizontal and vertical displacement which occurs presents
an added hazard where shipping channel space is at a premium.

With the advent of VLCCs a new dimension has been added
to the navigational problems of vessels. Until recently
ships were mostly in danger of running aground through coming
too close to the coast or to the sides of the channels.
Grounding was mostly a positional rather than a mid channel
draught problem. In the immediate approaches to ports and
hence in tidal waters where mid channel grounding was always
a periodical hazard, manoeuvring tended to be fairly closely
controlled by the port authorities who would also regulate
the number of vessels permitted to be in a minimum clearance
position at any one time. The VLCCs caused the size of the
areas of the sea where threshold depth clearance became
potentially as significant as in-channel position to expand
by several thousand square miles and, not surprisingly, the
basic information necessary to assess the extent of this
danger was found to be unavailable.

During the last decade, which has seen a massive increase
in hydrographic surveying effort, it has become evident that
the amplitudes of the seabed bathymetric features are appreciably larger than in the more sheltered areas near port waters.
As a consequence traditional surveying techniques, which were
developed to locate the lateral limits of channels, have
had to be modified. Whereas channel side gradients of 1:100
to 1:20 were expected, it came as an unpleasant surprise that

73

features with slopes as steep as 1:4 were by no means uncommon, and moreover the features producing these tended to lie across the lines of the channels rather than parallel to them.

It may appear obvious that a crossed sounding line pattern would long ago have shown these features, but as long as the need was not evident, there was no justification for an apparently time consuming duplication of effort. One cannot "read" the shape of the seabed as one can the landscape. Where no previous records exist, the difficulties cannot be assessed. Practical economic considerations have in the past led to the practice of collecting a progressively less dense set of data with increasing distance from base, or with increasing depth. This sometimes has produced the unfortunate implied conclusion that the shape of the seabed tends to become simpler with distance and depth (National Ports Council, 1977). There was an element of truth in this assumption insofar that the bases of current swept channels in estuaries often have gentle gradients through continuous scour. This is found not to apply to the terminal areas of channels, such as the entrance to Black Deep near the Long Sand, or to the Sandettie-Falls Banks, or Sandettie-Fairy Banks gaps. Each of these areas is characterised by a sandwave field of limited extent.

Similar areas occur in Malacca Straits, the entrance to Shatt al Arab, the West coast of Korea, Chesapeake Bay, etc..., none of which is any better charted   (Off, 1963).

It was only in 1967 that the existence of sandwaves was established in the northern approaches to Black Deep, the entrance to the Thames Estuary, by radically altering the sounding line pattern. Hitherto, the depths of this channel area between sandbanks were observed by running a set of parallel sounding lines from side to side. On the suspicion that a shoal bar extended across the channel mouth the pattern was reorientated, and a sandwave field was discovered on this then newly opened principal Thames fairway (Hydrographic Survey K506 1967, and Langhorne, 1973).

Note that surveys executed repeatedly over the preceding two centuries had not provided any clear indication of the presence of these features.

Because sandwaves can be 2 to 15 m high, and have "wavelengths" from 10 to 300 m, it is important that all crest-lines be found. In the last decade a valuable tool has become

widely available, and is now almost invariably used in hydrographic surveying. A sidescan sonar produces a pseudo-photo-
graphic image of a strip of seabed along the ship's track,
several hundred metres wide, building up the image line by
line (Fig. 1). The resulting records show the orientation
of the features and enable the surveyor to determine the
direction of his sounding lines so as to intersect the crestlines and hence to record their heights. Provided the crestlines are reasonably straight and level the survey is adequate
when each feature has been intersected. Not surprisingly,
however, such is not always the case; in fact, it is probably
rarely the case on terminal bars. Whenever a reasonably high
resolution sonar is used in an end of channel sandwave field,
a secondary sandwave pattern is invariably seen to be present.
This secondary pattern is much more difficult to measure
because it has not only a smaller wave-length of a few tens
of metres, but more importantly because it frequently has a
crestline orientation which is at a marked angle to that of
the major features. Consequently, undulations are found along
crestlines with wavelengths of 5 to 50 m, and to capture the
high points of these secondary patterns requires a much higher
line density than is either normal or practical in open sea
surveying.

Although sidescan sonar provides a means of measuring
the wavelength of secondary patterns, their height is less
easily determined. A comparison with sandwaves of similar
wavelength and observations by divers has indicated that they
are likely to have heights of 0.5 to 2 m. It follows that
when a survey is made in which the sounding line spacing is
wider than the wavelength, high points are bound to be missed.
Sample surveys have been made in the Sandettie Falls area to
saturation level (Cloet, 1976). Using a high precision positioning system, sounding lines were run at an average of 13 m apart,
whereas normal practice would place them 60 to 100 m apart.
The sample survey was completed in calm weather in the course
of 2 days to ensure that the sample itself was undisturbed
by sediment movement due to the time lapse between start and
finish. Using these data as a basis, standard line spacing
surveys have been simulated and it is evident that high spots,
as much as 1.5 to 2 m higher than the depths recorded in such
surveys, remain normally uncharted. Another similar survey
of the same area indicated high spots up to 3 m shallower
than would normally be charted. This includes an uncertainty
factor of about a ± 0.3 m due to a possible measurement error
arising from the limitations of tidal datum corrections.

Cloet

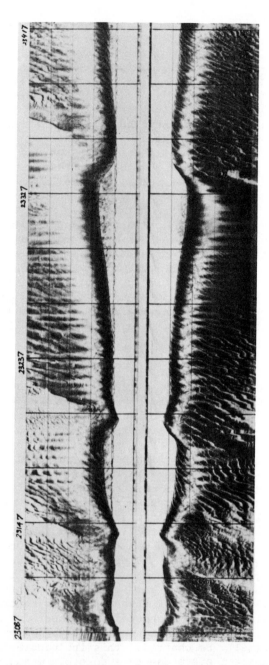

Fig. 1 Sandwave pattern in the Sandettie-Falls area

It would appear prudent, if these sample surveys are
not exceptional, for a minimum draught tolerance of 3 m to
be placed on critical channel depths because of potential
limitations of the coverage achieved in practical surveys. It
would be unrealistic to demand surveys of extensive areas
to be made on a line density equivalent to a ship's width
spacing, as was done here with existing equipment.

There has been prolonged controversy on the degree of
sandwave mobility (Langhorne, 1973; Ballade, 1953; Burton,
1977; Kirby and Kelland, 1972). Much of the uncertainty is
caused by insufficiently precise positioning systems, so
that the amount of apparent movement is of the same order as
the suspected positional accuracy limits, particularly where
the crestlines themselves have an undulating pattern. There
is also some confusion induced by nomenclature. The term
"sandwave" is at one time or another used for all features
from 0.5 to 15 m in height. Hence rates of movement from
5 to 150 m per year are quoted.

From the navigational point of view the positional displacement of a feature is to some extent irrelevant, because
if the point of critical depth moves even a few ship's lengths
down channel, but otherwise the depth value remains unaltered,
the extent of the hazard is unaltered because the navigational
chart is incapable of showing such differences.

Evidence is accumulating that the height of the crestlines
is not constant with time and that it can, at least on
occasion, shoal faster towards the mid channel area. Also
the same sandwave does not necessarily remain the highest,
whether or not it appears to undergo positional displacement.
There seems to be a tendency for the outer extremity of the
terminal bar to shoal, and the inner area to deepen, thus
effectively displacing the bar down channel. If further
investigation confirms that this pattern of movement persists,
the actual positional displacement of each wave feature would
seem to be less significant than the envelope of crestlines.
The hazard area would literally be seen to move from one
sandwave to the next, down channel and obliquely towards mid
channel. The sandwaves such as those in Sandettie are probably temporary stores for a residual down channel sediment
transport, which is neutralised at the end-channel location,
where the residual flow is also reversed. When the terminal
bar is breached the scoured material is taken up in the larger
scale sandbank circulation.

Some measure of the kind of change of the content of a
sandbank can be obtained indirectly from long time series of
hydrographic surveys in an area which is closely and frequentl
surveyed (Cloet, 1968). One such area is the Edinburgh
Channels in the Thames Estuary. It was the principal route
into the Thames and was closely surveyed over more than 150
years, until 1965. Because it is both difficult and positivel
dangerous to survey the tops of banks, even in these relativel
sheltered waters, a contribution of a few million cubic metres
is not measurable, but as a bank increases in height, it becomes more vulnerable to wave activity, so that the net effect
is an expansion of the area occupied. As discussed earlier,
hydrographic surveying has long paid particular attention to
the location of the shoal edges of channels. A careful
analysis of the dimensions of intercept areas at depth levels,
particularly critical for pre-war shipping, i.e., at 3 to 6
fathoms, shows that decadal size variations of an expanding
sandbank occur. (see Fig. 2). In the late 1950's and early
1960's the entrance to the then principal of the two Edinburgh
Channels, the North Edinburgh Channel, developed more shoal
heads and these were positionally unstable. The location of
this growing hazard area was an end channel terminal bar.
Fig. 3 shows that the cause of the trouble was a small migratir
sandbank, which travelled over a period of about 25 years to
reach this terminal position, where the residual flow of the
major Knock Deep channel caused it to migrate westward to

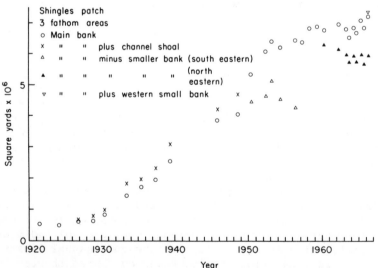

Fig. 2 Expansion of the Shingles Patch in the
Edinburgh Channels

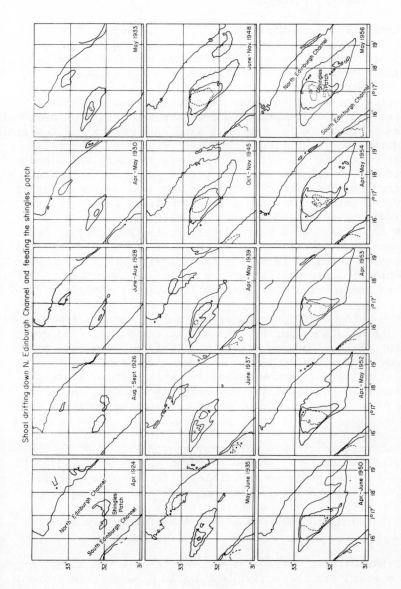

Fig. 3   Migrating shoal in the North Edinburgh Channel

become incorporated in the Middle Ground. Fig. 2 shows how
the growth of this larger bank was temporarily accelerated by
this contribution (Cloet,   1968).

Apart from such modifications, it is evident that the
growth curve is a cumulative normal curve suggesting that a
supply operated from a source which was accessible for only
a limited period. The event illustrated also appears to
support the contention that the terminal bars may have been
the supply routes along which less conspicuous quantities
migrated and it is tempting to describe these bars as sediment
bridges. Elsewhere, on the huge sandbank complex off Lowestoft
this circuitous migration of sediment from bank to bank is
further confirmed (Cloet, 1963). There is therefore a body
of evidence to support the theory that sediment in terminal
bar sandwaves can migrate laterally across a channel, but it
is decadal rather than annual in periodicity, and there are
some indications that seasonal variations in the rate of
growth do occur. On a year by year basis the seasonal variations mask the decadal circulation. Therefore, for practical
purposes, a detailed survey of the Sandettie-Falls terminal
bar contains observational errors which are as large, or larger
than the degree of annual instability (Cloet, 1968).

The bathymetric pattern of the seabed remains recognisable
for a usefully long period, even in mobile areas. The upper
position of the sandwave crests oscillate about a mean position
and undergo some residual displacement (Ballade, 1953). The
oscillation is only a few metres in amplitude and distorts
the crestline principally. The larger sandwaves, in excess
of 100 m in wavelength, tend to undergo proportionately only
minor modifications in their profiles.

· The texture of wave patterns seen on Fig. 1 shows the
relative complexity of seabed features with a wavelength of
about 10 m, which may be invisible to normal hydrographic
surveys. Langhorne (1973) has shown that those occurring
near the crestline may be obliterated by storm activity, but
that afterwards the pattern is restored fairly rapidly even
there.

Sandwaves with wavelengths larger than 100 m do not appear
to have moved significantly, bearing in mind the limitations
of the attainable accuracy of positioning systems. The crestlines may be displaced by 20 to 40m, but the pattern of the
features is only slightly and temporarily distorted

(Burton, 1977). Variations in height are of the order of about 1 m, which is rather less than the resolution capability of a normal hydrographic survey (Cloet, 1963).

In some cases, geological analysis has been used to demonstrate the long term stability of certain sandwave-like features. An undisturbed association of pollen, dating back about 3500 years, was found in the surface sediment of these (Kirby and Kelland, 1972; Kirby and Oele, 1975).

The differences between the shape and depths of an area 100m × 100m and a similarly sized neighbouring area tend to be more pronounced than between either and the same area 6 months later. If this should prove widely true, it could be used as a positioning method based on image to image correlation. Certainly people who operate repeatly in a certain area are able to recognise from their sidescan sonar whether or not they have reached the area in question.

This mode of navigation by correlation would require that the reference image, i.e., the hydrographic survey, is stored in a random access matrix. The correlating unit would be the sub-area sample currently being collected by the navigator. The system could not be expected to work where the seabed was perfectly level in all directions, but this is very rarely the case, particularly in congested waters, because congestion tends to exist where the complexity of the shape of the seabed causes the usable fairway to be restricted.

Evidently the production of magnetic memory charts would be a major undertaking and is only to be contemplated if significant advantages ensue. On the other hand close quarters navigation tends to occur in sea areas' which are frequently re-examined and therefore updating of such areas would be completed in a reasonably short time. The more intractable problem would be for a sufficient number of ships to be suitably equipped to make use of the facility.

As has already been discussed, a hydrographic survey of a navigationally critical area normally establishes the depth of about 5% of the survey area. The sample "saturation" surveys inspected about 30% and showed topographic roughness of ± 2 to 3 m in excess of that seen by normal surveys. The fair sheet is the graphical record of the digital information, and is the only permanent and accessible record of the survey. The line spacing adopted is normally a function of the paper space occupied by a three digit number. Hence a survey to be

rendered on a scale of 1/15000 can have soundings no closer
than about 2 and 5 mm apart, i.e., 30 m ground distance in
line, and 75 m across line. It also follows that on a survey
on this scale, less than 1% of the height information of the
seabed is permanently recorded. None of this produces any
hazard for the user, if the surveyor has obtained
the minimum depths. Features with amplitudes of 5 to 6 m and
wavelengths of less than 60 to 120 m are barely identifiable.

The navigational chart is a graphical instrument which
contains a great deal of above water information. It is without exception intended to aid positioning. Depth data are
by comparison very sketchy. A chart does not normally have
soundings closer than 1 cm apart, i.e., in critical areas no
closer than 500 m apart. In fact these depth values are only
intended as local danger point indicators, and the metre lines
are not contours but danger lines. The latter are always
biased to exaggerate the shoal area for added safety. Since
critical areas, such as Sandettie, have complex surfaces, the
navigator of the ship negotiating the constricted channel
cannot relate the information from the echo sounder to the
chart. He has to have recourse to position information,
obtained from a ranging system, transfer it to the chart and
then conclude from the track which so develops whether he is
closing in to danger. The process is slow and it is eminently
sensible to give the danger line as wide as berth as possible.
The positioning system used for track plotting on the chart
is probably shore based, and though normally accurate to
100 m, it can produce errors of 500 m. In addition radar
ranges on buoys may be used, but the cable scope of these is
such that no greater accuracy of position can be achieved
from their use. It is easy to understand why the depth information is only used in such a restricted manner, but consequently an imminent grounding hazard can only be recognised
indirectly from a plot on the chart.

A magnetic memory chart would possibly not be a complete
substitute for the traditional navigational chart but a means
of providing access to information which cannot at present be
made readily accessible. It would become possible to display
the depth profile which should develop along the projected tra
More than that the navigator could rehearse himself through a
close quarter situation well before reaching the critical area
as if he were operating a "telesonic" system. Perhaps the maj
advantage might be the independence from signals transmitted
to the ship, which can always be suspected of having become

unreliable, because the ship's officers do not have any means of maintaining the efficient functioning of the navigational system.

REFERENCES

Ballade, P. "Study of sandwaves of the Loire Estuary, their character and evaluation", *Comite Central d'Oceanographic Bull. d'Information*, **5**, 1953.

Burton, B. W. "An investigation of a sandwave field at the South Western end of the Sandettie Bank Dover Strait", *Int. Hydrogr. Review*, Monace LIV (2), July 1977.

Cloet, R. L. "The effect of line spacing on the survey accuracy in a sandwave area", *The Hydrographic Journal*, 1976.

Cloet, R. L. "The Development of the Edinburgh Channels of the Outer Thames Estuary - A problem of sediment circulation", Ph.D. Thesis, London University, 1968.

Cloet, R. L. "Hydrographic Analysis of the sandbanks in the Approaches to Lowestoft Harbour", Admiralty Marine Science Publication No. 6, 1963.

"Hydrographic Surveying in Ports and Approaches and its Automation", National Ports Council, 1977.

"Hydrographic survey of Approaches to the Outer Thames", K5064.

Kirby, R. and Kelland, N. C. "Adjacent stable and apparently mobile linear sediment ridges in the Southern North Sea", *Nature, Physical Science*, **238**, 1972.

Kirby, R. and Oele, E. "The Geological history of the Sandettie-Fairy Bank area, Southern North Sea", *Phil. Trans. Roy. Soc, A.*, 1975.

Länghorne, D. N. "The anatomy of a sandwave field", M.Sc. Thesis, Dept. Physics, University of Bath, 1973.

Off, T. "Rhythmic linear sand bodies caused by tidal currents", *Am. Assoc. Pet. Geol. Bull.*, **47**, 1963.

THE JAPANESE APPROACH TO MARINE TRAFFIC ENGINEERING

Y. Iijima

(Tokyo University of Mercantile Marine, Japan)

1. INTRODUCTION

About 20 years ago, even the number of ships operating
in any area of the world was not known with any precision.
Since 1960, however, as the world economy has increased, so
also has both the size and the number of ships at sea. Marine
traffic has become heavily congested. The systematic study
of this traffic, with the main purpose of improving safety
and efficiency at sea, began in Japan at about this time.

The first task was to observe the actual traffic situation, both visually and by radar, in narrow channels and
canals. These surveys enabled basic traffic features, such
as traffic volume, density, speed and ship size distribution
and track, to be statistically analysed. The study then
gradually developed to higher levels to deal with applications
such as traffic capacity, ship safety domain, design of ship
lanes and control systems. Fig. 1 indicates the Japanese
approach to marine traffic studies.

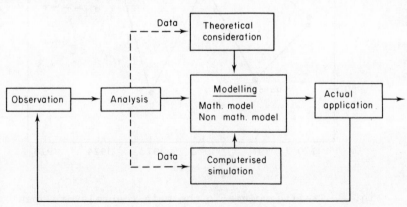

Fig. 1   An approach to marine traffic studies

D

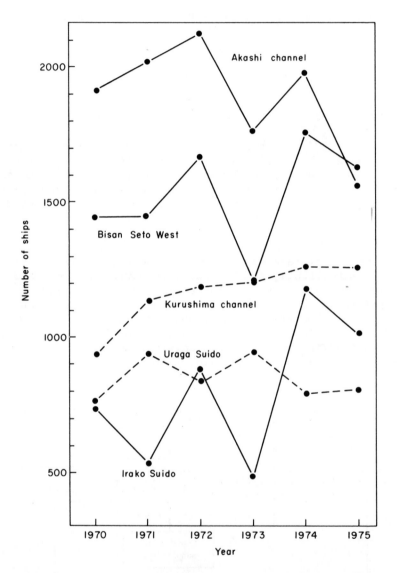

Fig. 2 Traffic volume in the main channels of Japan

In this paper, four main categories of study - the results of traffic observations, traffic capacity, sea casualties and traffic control - are briefly described.

2. TRAFFIC OBSERVATIONS AND THEIR RESULTS

2.1 Traffic volume

The traffic volume in the main Japanese channels is shown in Fig. 2.

2.2 Traffic pattern

The space distribution of traffic in a multi-directional area may be shown as a track chart (Fig. 3), a gate diagram (Fig. 4) or a vane diagram (Fig. 5). The time pattern may be shown as the number of ships pasing through a transit line across a channel within a certain time interval. Fig. 6 shows the observations, and two Fourier series approximations.

From this distribution, we can see that the peak of traffic volume is dependent on the time of day, i.e. the working time at the harbour. If, however, we examine the situation over a short time interval, say 5 or 10 minutes, the traffic volume follows a Poisson distribution as in Fig. 7. It follows that the intervals between successive arrivals at a certain point of the channel are exponentially distributed as shown in Fig. 8 and that the arrival of a ship in a short period is a random phenomenon.

2.3 Speed distribution

It has been observed that the speed distribution of ships, when navigating freely, is approximately Gaussian, and that both the average speed and the standard deviation decrease with poorer visibility.

2.4 Use of records of course recorder

The frequency of steering and course changes of a ship passing through a certain channel may be considered as a danger factor, and may be caused by bends in the channel, collision avoidance or deviation from route due to wind and current. Such data have been collected from course recorders and analysed so as to evaluate a danger factor, such as a collision probability, using queueing theory (Hara (1971, 1973).

Fig. 3   Track chart in Tokyo Bay (by Oikawa)

2.5 Traffic density

Ship density distribution may depend on the utility and
the danger of an area. Fig. 9 is an example of a normal type
density distribution over an area; Fig. 10 shows crossing
density only.

2.6 Relationship between speed, traffic volume and density

The volume of traffic, Q, passing through a given
channel in unit time can be expressed as

$$Q = \rho.V_s \qquad (1)$$

where ρ is the density of shipping and V_s is the average ship
speed. The relationship between them can be shown graphically

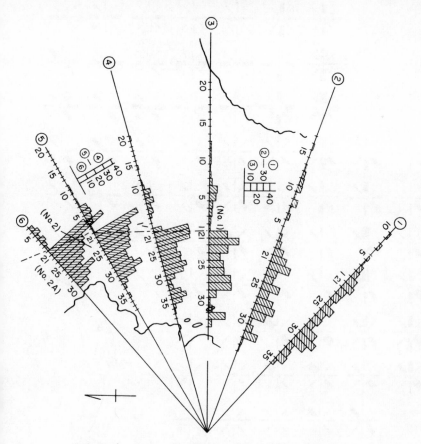

Fig. 4   Gate diagram of traffic pattern

as in Figs. 11 and 12.

3.   TRAFFIC CAPACITY

3.1   Definition of capacity

It is considered that a ship is navigated so as to carry her own safety area around her. This area is called a ship safety domain or simply a ship domain. The maximum density, ρ_{max}, in a channel occurs when the safety domains are tightly packed; the maximum capacity, C_{max}, is then given by

$$C_{max} = \rho_{max} \cdot V_s \cdot W \qquad (2)$$

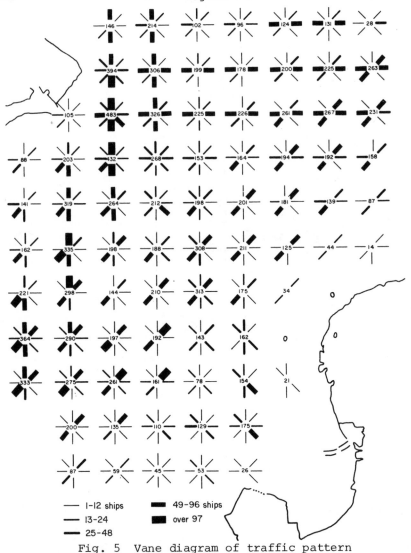

Fig. 5   Vane diagram of traffic pattern

where W is the lane width.

    This capacity may be regarded as the basic, or ideal, traffic capacity, but it is difficult for ships to navigate in this condition. The capacity up to which ships can easily navigate in ordinary conditions is referred to as the actual traffic capacity, considering wind and current or fog conditions. The capacities which are used in designing a fairway and control systems can be derived from multiplying the basic traffic capacity by a suitable factor.

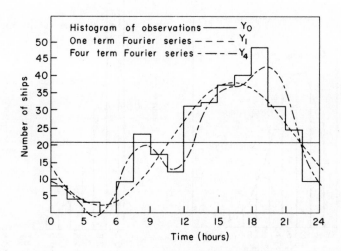

Fig. 6   Time pattern and Fourier series approximations
(by Makishima)

3.2 *Ship safety domain*

A ship safety domain is not only useful as described
above, but is also important in relation to collision avoidance manoeuvres and collision avoidance equipment. The domain
is obtained from traffic observations and theoretical studies
based on the dynamic characteristics of the ship. There are
two ways of calculating the size of the domain from the observations. One makes use of the region of high ship density
around the ship of interest (Fujii et al. (1966), Goodwin
(1975)); the other utilises the relative tracks of other ships
as shown in Fig. 13 (Iijima (1967)).

The ship safety domain is generally approximated to a
half ellipse with the long axis, r, from the ship's head to
stern, the short axis, s, across the ship. Both r and s may
be expressed as functions of ship length, L; relative length,
L_r; own ship speed and relative speed, V and V_r; meeting angle
of both ships, θ; geographical condition, e.g. a channel or
an open sea, G; weather conditions, W; and so on. Thus

$$r(\text{or } s) = f\ (L, L_r, V, V_r, \theta, G, W,\ \ldots) \qquad (3)$$

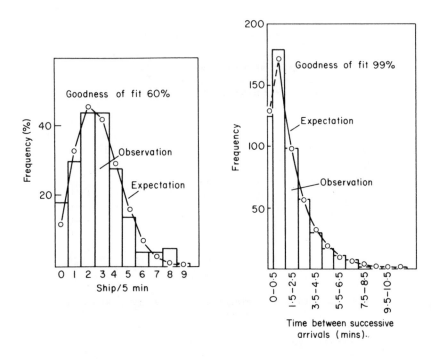

Fig. 7 Poisson distribution Fig. 8 Exponential distributi

Values of r and s have been obtained in specific conditions
such as the open sea, a narrow channel, overtaking and crossing. For example, values of r = 8.5L and s = 3.5L have been
obtained in the case of overtaking in a narrow channel (Fujii
(1970) Oshima et al. (1972), Sugisaki (1972)).

3.3 Conversion factor between ship size

     In order to obtain traffic capacity theoretically or by
computerised simulation, a ship of standard size is generally
used. Then the traffic capacity of the standard ship is distributed among the various classes of ship size using a conversion factor, which is a function of L/L_s, where L is a shi
length of a certain class and L_s is a ship length of the
standard ship.

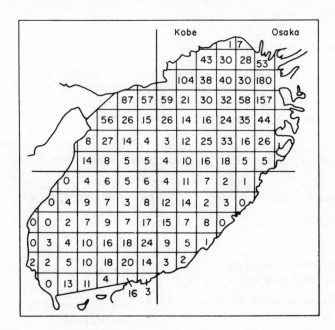

Fig. 9 Ship density diagram in Osaka Bay (by Yamaguchi et al.)

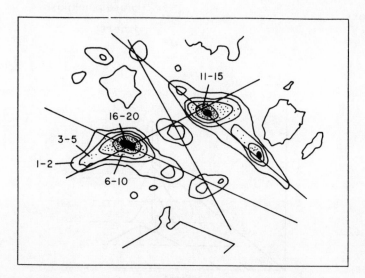

Fig. 10 Density diagram of ships crossing within 3 minutes
(by Hirano)

4. SEA CASUALTIES

4.1 Statistics

Figs..14 and 15 show the number of ships which require to be rescued after becoming a casualty during recent years, classified by type of casualty and the sea situation. We have studied the three main conjested areas of traffic in Japan - Uraga Suido, Irako Suido and Seto Inland Seas - where about 30% of the total casualties in Japan have occurred. Causes of casualty in 1975 are shown as follows.

mis-manoeuvre				
poor manoeuvre	11.6%	bad handling of engine	16.6%
poor lookout	8.7		
poor positioning	6.9	bad material and construction	11.3
carelessness because of weather and sea conditions	6.0	an Act of God	9.2
poor maintainance of hull and instruments	3.4	careless handling of imflammable materials	6.0
poor investigation of ship route	2.3	bad stowage	3.1
others	11.6	causes unknown	2.9
		others	0.4

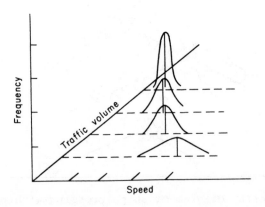

Fig. 11 Relationship between traffic volume and speed

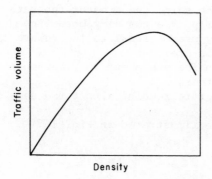

Fig. 12   Relationship between density and traffic volume

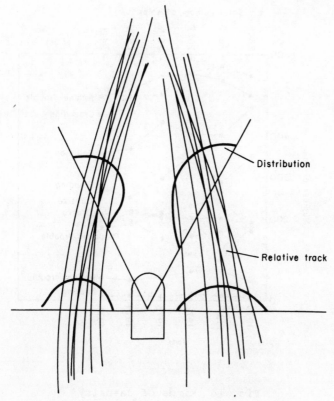

Fig. 13   Ship safety domain in overtaking

4.2   Studies of sea casualties

The following conclusions have emerged.

a.   The bigger the ship, the greater the rate of accident.
b.   The probability of a casualty occurring in a certain area approximately proportional to the square of the ship density in the area.
c.   Collisions in fog are about 90 times more frequent than in clear weather.
d.   The casualty rate remains almost the same from year to year.
These results are illustrated in Fig. 16.

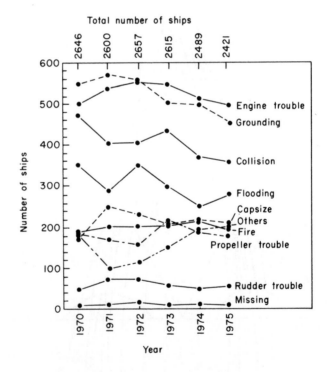

Fig. 14   Kinds of casualty

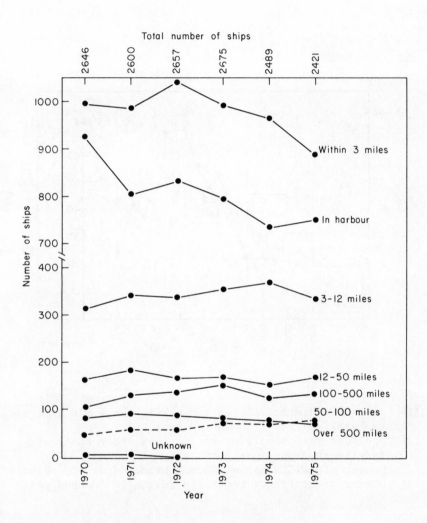

Fig. 15   Area of casualty

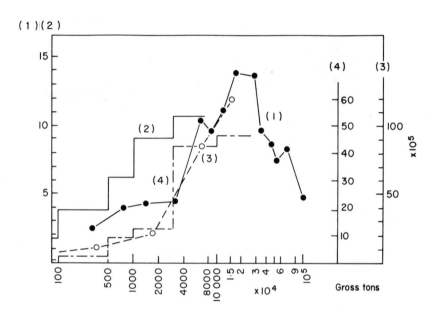

(1)   serious accident rate of tankers in the world (per total tankers)
(2)   accident rate requiring rescue; passenger boats and ferries in Japan (per total ships)
(3)   number of collisions at Kanmon strait (per 10^5 ships)
(4)   number of accidents requiring rescue in 70 open ports in Japan per 10^5 ships)

accident rate = (No. of accident ships in one year/total ship) x 100

Fig. 16   Relationship between ship size and accident
(by Shiobara)

Fujii derived theoretically the following formula for the number of collisions, N_{col}, in a certain area,

$$N_{col} = \int_0^T \int_S \int_L \int_{L'} \int_{\vec{V}} \int_{\vec{V'}} \; 1/2 \; \rho^2 \; |v-v'| \; dS \; dt \; dL \; dL' \; dV \; dV' \tag{4}$$

(the notation in this formula is given in *J. Royal Inst. Navigation*, 1971, **24**, No. 4, 539).

4.4 *Human factors in casualties*

The strain on ships officers during manoeuvring has been tested by observing pulse and mental reaction (Kuroda (1967). The report notes an increase of pulse rate when:

a. manoeuvring information increases;
b. reliable manoeuvring information is not available;
c. the officer makes his decision to manoeuvre;
d. the officer avoids another ship.

These findings may have some relationship with the following results obtained from captains who suffered casualties in 1959 and 1960 (Japanese Association for preventing Marine Accidents (1971)).

Physical or mental condition of captain when accident occured	small ship (289)	large ship (381)
poor thinking due to insufficient sleep or over-work	22.1 %	31.5 %
hesitation in decision	17.3	16.5
forgotten navigational knowledge	2.7	1.6
forgotten pre-planned manoeuvring order	3.1	4.7
mis-manoeuvre owing to emergency situation	10.7	24.9
over-confidence	21.5	28.1
failure to change decision because of concern for captain's dignity	3.5	3.1
neglected his men's advice	3.1	5.0
fear of causing inconvenience to crew	7.3	10.2
severe schedule	12.5	15.5
left manoeuvre to his men	12.1	11.5
stuck to pre-plan	10.7	13.1
made inadequate use of navigational aids	18.3	32.5
too much concern for a specific ship	20.4	27.3
too much concern for an obstacle on the route	14.9	13.9

5. VESSEL TRAFFIC CONTROL SYSTEM

The traffic control system generally consists of a traffic scheme and an information system.

5.1 Traffic schemes

The following factors should be taken into consideration when designing traffic schemes:

a. traffic volume
b. traffic density
c. lane width
d. ship average speed
e. queue at crossing area
f. curvature of lane
g. distance to destination (time needed to destination)
h. danger factor
i. natural conditions such as wind and current
j. harbour facilities such as anchorage
k. navigational law concerned.

Various traffic schemes at Tokyo Bay have been studied. Fig. 17 shows an example of a scheme in which the traffic volume and the danger factor are simulated using a computer. One of the most important factors is the queue of traffic at a crossing point. This problem has been studied by means of queueing theory as well as by computerised simulation.

5.2 Information and control systems

Special traffic regulations, primarily designed to ensu: safety, are now in operation in the three most congested area in Japan already mentioned. However, safety alone is not enough, and traffic control and information systems have been partially applied, or are planned, in some areas. The Traffi Centre at Tokyo Bay, which was opened in February 1977, is regarded as a prototype of other control systems in the futur The Tokyo scheme is not yet complete, and an integrated syste involving both traffic control and harbour facilities is planned.

6. CONCLUSION

The Japanese approach to marine traffic engineering is briefly described. Current research activities for marine traffic in Japan are being carried out by specialists in many

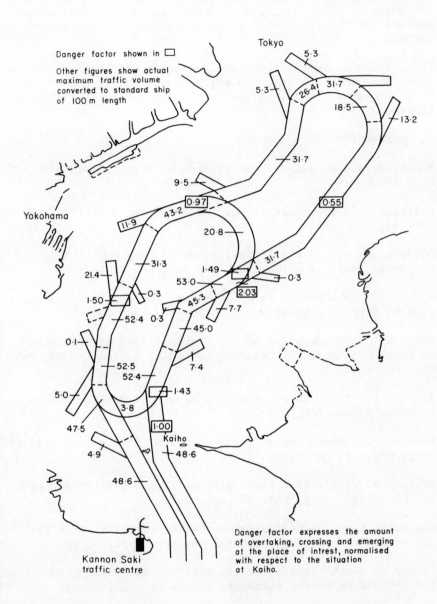

Fig. 17 Ideal traffic scheme in Tokyo Bay

different fields, who are attacking the problems with their
own methods. They all have a common aim; to develop methods
whereby traffic phenomena can be expressed in quantitative
terms.

I cannot help remembering the words of the great scien-
tist, Lord Kelvin, "It could not be said that it has truely
been understood, unless a phenomenon could be quantitatively
expressed.

7. REFERENCES

Fujii, Y. and et al. "Effective Area of Ships", *JNSL*, Vol. 35,
Jul. 1966.

Fujii, Y. "A Consideration on the Effective domain", *JNSL*,
Vol. 44, Oct. 1970.

Goodwin, E. M. "A Statistical Study of Ship Domains", *J. of
the Royal Inst. of Navigation,* Vol. 28, No. **3**, 1975.

Hara, K. "On a Method to Estimate the Probabilities of Collision of Ship in Any Fairways", *JNSL*, Vol. 46, Dec. 1971.

Hara, K. "Consideration to the Probabilities of Collision
of Ships by a model of Collision Avoiding system", *JNSL*, Vol.
50, Dec. 1973.

Iijima, Y. "Ship Safety domain", Report of Traffic condition
in Uraga Suido, Dec. 1967.

Kuroda, T. "Experimental Study on Mental Strain of Navigators"
JNSL, Vol. 38, Dec. 1967.

Oshima, R. et al. "The Evasion Diameter and Effective Domain
for Crossing", *JNSL,* Vol. 47, Aug. 1972.

Sugisaki, A. M. "A Consideration on the Occlusive Area in
Marine Traffic Flow", *JNSL,* Vol. 48, Dec. 1972.

"Study on Marine Traffic Safety System", The Japan Association
for Preventing Marine Accident, Report of 1971, *JNSL.*

DETERMINATION OF SHIP DOMAIN SIZE

E. M. Goodwin

(Marine Traffic Research Unit, City of London Polytechnic)

INTRODUCTION

One of the fundamental concepts which may be considered in any investigation of marine traffic flows is that of a ship domain. This may be defined as the effective area around a ship which a navigator would like to keep free with respect to other ships and stationary objects. This area will not be the same size and shape for all ships but will depend on a variety of factors such as the speed and size of the ship, and the density of traffic and physical constraints in the particular waters in which the ship is navigating. The domain may thus be considered as the water area required by any one ship at any one time for safe and efficient navigation.

THE PROJECT

About 5 years ago a project was started at the City of London Polytechnic with the initial aim of establishing that ship domains did exist and determining methods of identifying them; with the second aim of evaluating their size and shape under different conditions. This paper considers the various methods investigated for identifying and then evaluating the parameters of a ship domain as part of the initial aim of the project. Information is still being collected on the second part and will continue for several years as there are so many factors to be considered. The project also has a third stage which is to apply the appropriate values to various problems in marine traffic flow; work is being done on this too.

There would seem to be two fundamental approaches to investigating the concept of a ship domain. One, which is basically theoretical, is to build a mathematical model based on knowledge of a ship's manoeuvring equations. The other, a more empirical approach, is based on observations of the behaviour of navigators in marine traffic flows. This second approach was the one adopted and hence the project was of a statistical nature.

SOURCES OF DATA

Two sources of data were used for the original work. One was recordings of the performance of ships' officers in colli-sion avoidance exercises on a marine radar simulator, the second was a series of marine traffic surveys conducted in an area of the North Sea around the Sunk lightvessel. Ships' officers at varying stages of their careers come to the Poly-technic for a week's course in radar methods of navigation using the marine radar simulator. At the time of this work the simulator was a Solartron three own-ship model consisting of three separate booths each equipped with a radar display and controls by which the student or group of students could alter the speed and course of the ship he is navigating. The instructor from his master console had up to four moving tar-gets and other stationary targets over which he had direct control. The simulator incorporated a Kelvin-Hughes "photoplot device whereby a filmed recording of an exercise could be made and then a projection of the positions of all the ships in the playing area at selected intervals could be shown. From this a tracing of a complete exercise could be taken afte its finish. During the course the ships' officers worked through a series of exercises on collision avoidance set in three different areas, viz., the open ocean, the Straits of Gibraltar and the Dover Strait. All the exercises were assume to take place in fog with visibility of ¼ nautical mile since this is a typical situation when a navigator must rely on his radar display and not on visual observations. All discussions between instructor and students were deferred until after an exercise had been completed so it was felt that the manoeuvres undertaken were reasonably typical of what the navigator would have done himself in a similar real-life situation at sea. Fig. 1 shows a tracing of one of the completed exercises set in the Dover Strait. In total plots of 70 exercises were analysed .

The marine traffic surveys were carried out on board the M.V. "Sir John Cass", the research vessel of the School of Navigation at the City of London Polytechnic. This is a 154 ton ship, 100 feet in length, which is mainly used for radar training in the river Thames but is also made available for research projects. There are three radar screens on board for teaching purposes so it is possible to use one for a sur-vey without hindering the navigation of the ship. The area in which the surveys were conducted is in the North Sea about 12 miles from Harwich. As shown in Fig. 2 it covers an inter-section of the routes from East coast ports to North-West

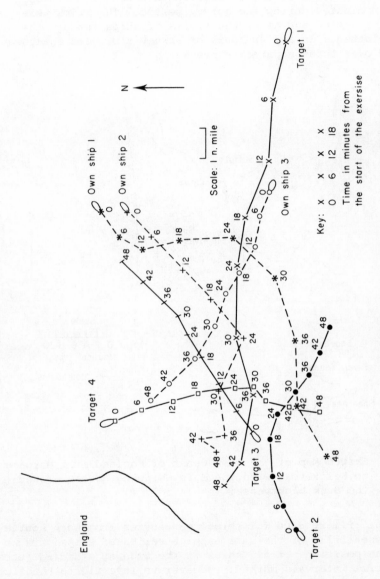

Fig. 1 Dover Strait: Exercise 20: One Development of the Situation

Europe and the English Channel and thus has a high traffic
density with traffic converging from all directions. Photographs were taken of a 3 cm wavelength marine radar display
every 3 minutes during the survey period. The films were
later projected and hence the tracks of ships through the area
were plotted. In all 48 hours of survey time were analysed
spread over three separate surveys.

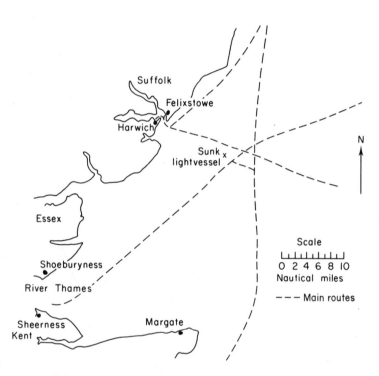

Fig. 2   Sketch Map of the East Coast of England from Margate
to Felixstowe with the Main Shipping Routes around
the Sunk Lightvessel

The primary data for ships' manoeuvres from each source
were essentially of the same type: a series of ships' tracks
with the positions of all ships in the area at standard successive time intervals marked. However to investigate the size
and shape of a ship domain the behaviour of ships relative
to each other had to be examined. For any one ship, the distance and relative bearing of all other ships in its vicinity
at any given time can be ascertained. Thus the distribution

of the other ships around the central ship at that time can
be plotted. The process is repeated for several successive
instants of time and the different distributions so obtained
are superimposed. In this way a picture can be built up representative of a variety of ships and times. Fig. 3 shows a
typical such distribution, the line of reference for each
central ship at any time being the direction of the ship's
head at that time. The clear area of water around the central
ship, the ship domain, may be seen in the figure.

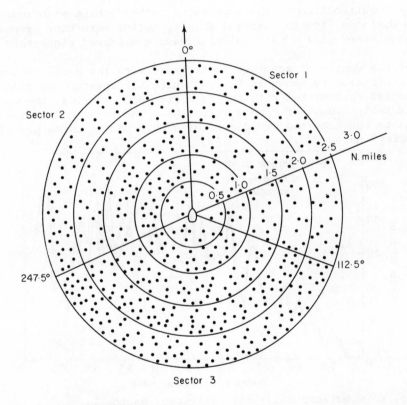

Fig. 3 Distribution of other ships around the central ship
        (Sunk Survey 1)

Consideration of the International Regulations for the
Prevention of Collisions at Sea, which give different procedures
for collision avoidance when the threats are on different
bearings, suggests that the area around the central ship is
not homogeneous and should be broken into three separate sectors
as shown in Fig. 3. These may be defined in terms of θ, the

bearing of the "other" ship from the central ship, as:

Sector 1: $0^° \leqslant \theta < 112.5^°$ - starboard sector

Sector 2: $247.5^° \leqslant \theta < 360^°$ - port sector

Sector 3: $112.5^° \leqslant \theta < 247.5^°$ - astern sector.

The areas of these sectors are in the ratios 5:5:6.

Distributions of the numbers of "other" ships with respect to distance from the central ship by sector were thus prepared. Range steps of $\frac{1}{10}$ nautical mile were considered since this was the degree of accuracy justifiable with the data. A typica distribution is shown in Fig. 4, which illustrates the major problem encountered with the data from both sources, the considerable amount of random variation. The problem therefore was to evaluate the boundaries of a ship domain using practical "noisy" data.

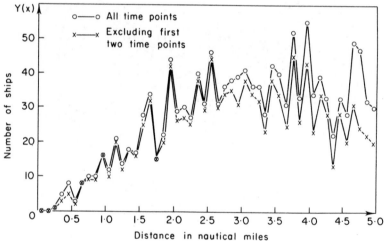

Fig. 4   Simulator Data: All exercises: Sector 2:
The distribution of ships around a central ship:
Actual results

THE MAIN HYPOTHESIS

The distributions of numbers of ships were observed in concentric annuli around the "central ship" with mean radii starting at $\frac{1}{20}$ nautical mile and increasing by $\frac{1}{10}$ nautical mil to $4\frac{19}{20}$ nautical miles. Thus the areas involved were in the ratio:

1:3:5:7:.........:   2r-1:......:99 where r is the rth area
from the centre.

The main hypothesis is that if the presence of a central
ship has no effect on the position of other ships, then the
distribution of other ships over the area should be uniform.
Hence if K is the uniform density per square mile in the area
under observation, the actual numbers in successive annuli
should be:

$$\frac{K\pi}{100}\ ,\ \frac{3K\pi}{100},\ \frac{5K\pi}{100},\ \ldots\ \frac{(2r-1)K\pi}{100},\ \ldots\ \frac{99K\pi}{100}\ .$$

If the discussion is confined to one of the sectors only,
then assuming no effect of the central ship, the numbers in a
sector will be proportional to the area of that sector. Hence
if a constant α is defined dependent on the over-all density
of shipping and the size of sector, then for any one sector
the number of ships in successive annuli will be:

$$\alpha,\ 3\alpha,\ 5\alpha,\ \ldots\ (2r-1)\alpha,\ \ldots\ 99\alpha.$$

Assuming that ships within an annulus are also uniformly
distributed, then taking an annulus of width δx and of inner
radius x the number of ships within it will be given by
$\alpha(x+\delta x)^2 - \alpha x^2$, which tends to $2\alpha x$ as δx tends to 0. Hence
the curve of increase of numbers of ships (i.e. the annulus
distribution) is given by the line y = $2\alpha x$ <u>if no domain exists.</u>

However <u>if there is a domain</u>, the curve may be expected
to be of the form shown in Fig. 5 where y_d, the annular distribution of the number of ships in the presence of the domain,
is given by

$$y_d < 2\alpha x \text{ for } 0 < x < x_A$$
$$y_d > 2\alpha x \text{ for } x_A < x. < x_c$$

$$y_d = 2\alpha x \text{ for } x \geqslant x_c$$

$$\text{and}\quad y_d = 2\alpha x \text{ for } x = x_A.$$

The ships which would have been in the area defined by
$0 < x < x_A$, must have moved into the area defined by $x_A < x < x_c$.

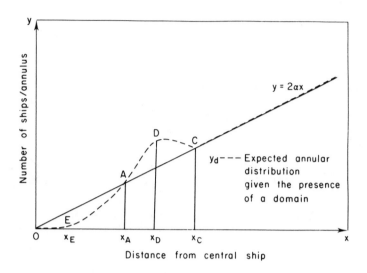

Fig. 5   Distribution of ships given the presence of a domain

$x = x_A$ defines the value of x for which $y_d = 2\alpha x$ for the first time. For $x \geqslant x_C$ the effect of the disturbance is over and the situation has stablised.

THE RANGE OF THE DOMAIN BOUNDARY

Various alternative definitions have been considered for the range of the domain boundary which will be referred to as the "domange". The simplest definition could be the nearest distance that anyone is observed to go (x_E in Fig. 5). This is not satisfactory for several reasons; thus it could be distorted by one extreme value and so would not reflect the attitude of the majority of navigators.

Another fairly simple definition would be to take the distance below which only an arbitrary figure, such as 10% or 5%, of all ships are observed to go. However, this was thought to be to arbitrary and was difficult to use in practic

Fujii and Tanaka (1971) use a physical analogy of two particles with like electric charges approaching each other to define the domange. The repulsive force increases as the sepa ration decreases. Thus one can assume a potential field aroun

a ship which causes an imaginary repulsive force for approaching ships and a weak attractive force for distant ships.
For a simplified situation where all ships are travelling in
the same direction Fig. 6 shows the stream lines of other ships
around a central ship under this hypothesis. However there
appears to be little logical basis why ships at a certain distance should be attracted to the central ship. Fig. 7 shows
an expected density curve if one considers a semi-cross-section
OQ of the stream lines. The domange according to Fujii is
taken to be the distance x_B at which the density is maximised.

This definition is considered to be too conservative and in
practice the kurtosis of typical curves is such that the maximum is not well defined particularly in the presence of noise.
In practice it is easier to work with numbers of ships rather
than densities. Hence this definition could be modified
slightly to be the distance at which the numbers of ships are
locally maximised, giving x_D in Fig. 5.

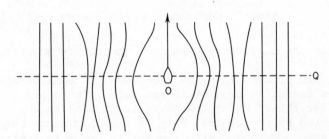

Fig. 6 Wake lines of ships around a central ship

In this project it was decided to define the domange as
the distance x_A of Fig. 5, where for the first time the number
of ships observed is what would have been expected given no
disturbing influence. This is also the first point at which
the density reaches the over-all density level. It has the
important advantage of a simple operational interpretation
as making a boundary within which the presence of the central
ship causes a depletion in the expected number of other ships
and immediately outside which there is an enhancement in the
expected number of other ships. A further advantage is that
a crossing point such as A is easier to locate than a maximum
such as D.

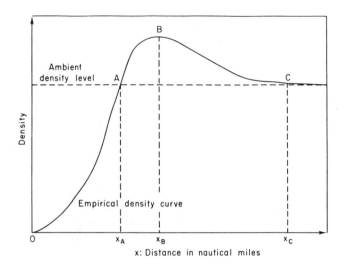

Fig. 7 Empirical density curve

METHODS OF CALCULATING THE RANGE OF THE DOMAIN BOUNDARY

The main problem to be overcome was the considerable amoun
of random variation present in the data. There are many
reasons for this. First the ships in an area at any time are
not affected by the central ship in question alone but by each
other's presence, hence with respect to one ship the positions
of the others are not really independent. Secondly by looking
at the situation every 6 minutes there will be a connection
between successive positions of two ships relative to each
other, which with small relative velocities can lead to a concentration of points. Thirdly there is the common statistical
problem of having to measure continuous data in discrete class

Data from the simulator had two additional main faults.
First the fact that the initial positions of an exercise are
predetermined means that there will be certain points in the
distributions where the various exercises stop. These are
removed to a certain extent, but not completely, by the omission
from the analysis of the positions at time points 0 and 6
minutes (see Fig. 4). This procedure also meant that only
positions for which the navigator had had a chance to assess
the situation were included. Secondly since the exercises
were in collision avoidance, once the collision threats were
negotiated no further ships tended to be introduced, with a

twofold result that the density of ships fell off at large
distances and there was an under-representation in Sector 3.

The main factor leading to noise in the survey data was
the loss of radar targets as the distance from the centre of
the radar screen, x, increases. The loss is proportional to
x^4 as a general rule but varies considerably with the type of
target. Additionally the existence of routes in the survey
area as determined by Goodwin and Kemp (1977) means that the
assumption of uniform distribution becomes spurious especially
at larger distances. The chosen method for determining the
domanges should therefore concentrate on the smaller distances
where the data accord with the hypothesis more reliably.

1. *Graphical Methods*

One approach to the problem is to estimate the domange by
graphical methods, but the data need to be smoothed first.

Several smoothing methods, e.g. exponential and various
weighted average schemes, were tried, but the simplest was
found to be sufficient in practice. This was a three point
central moving average with fixed weights. The equation
$E(x) = \frac{1}{3}\left[Y(x-1) + Y(x) + Y(x+1) \right]$ was used most frequently,

where $E(x)$ is the smoothed value and $Y(x)$ the actual value at
distance x.

Having smoothed the data the line of uniform density must
be drawn on the graph, but it was felt that a traditional method
such as least squares fit was not completely appropriate here.

One solution is to draw subjectively a line of best fit.

A second is to estimate the value of α for the line of
uniform density $y = 2\alpha x$. The total number of ships expected
in the total area of outer radius x_i is αx_i^2. Hence if C_i is
the total number of ships observed in that area: $C_i = \hat{\alpha} x_i^2$,
giving $\hat{\alpha} = C_i/x_i^2$ where $\hat{\alpha}$ is the estimated value of α.

Inspection of the curves suggested that 2.5n miles was a
suitable figure to take for x_i, but as it was an arbitrary

choice it was felt that further methods should be sought. Table I shows some results obtained for x_A and x_D by this method and compares them with those obtained by drawing a line of best fit subjectively.

Table I

The domain boundaries obtained by graphical methods using different definitions, in nautical miles

	SECTOR 1	SECTOR 2	SECTOR 3
A: SIMULATOR DATA: ALL EXERCISES			
x_A Line by calculation	1.37	1.35	0.45
x_A Line of best fit	1.04	1.35	0.45
x_D Line by calculation	2.05	1.85	0.65
B: SUNK SURVEY DATA: SURVEY 2			
x_A Line by calculation	0.84	0.85	0.70
x_A Line of best fit	0.84	0.85	0.65
x_D Line by calculation	2.45	1.95	1.25

x_A distance at which number of ships first equals expected number

x_D distance at which number of ships is locally maximised

2. A specified equation of the displacement curve

Various attempts were made to fit a curve that might produce reasonable results. However the form of the curve was not immediately obvious as there were so many unknown parameters. The most reasonable equation seemed to be that of a sine curve superimposed on a straight line, as a sine curve has the automatic property of producing decreases then compensating increases.

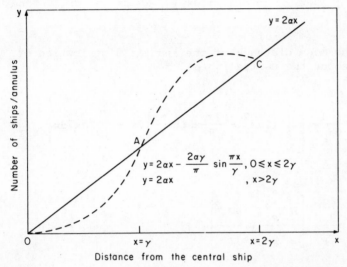

Fig. 8 A sine curve form displacement and its extension to give a possible distribution of ships around a central ship

The equation tried was:

$$y = 2\alpha x - \beta \sin \frac{\pi x}{\gamma}, \quad 0 \leqslant x \leqslant 2\gamma.$$

To make the curve parallel to the x axis at $x = 0$ we require $\beta = \dfrac{2\alpha\gamma}{\pi}$

giving
$$\left.\begin{array}{ll} y = 2ax - \dfrac{2\alpha\gamma}{\pi} \sin \dfrac{\pi x}{\gamma} , & 0 \leqslant x \leqslant 2\gamma \\[3mm] y = 2\alpha x, & 2\gamma < x \end{array}\right\} .$$

This equation implies that $x = \gamma$ at A, $x = 2\gamma$ at C, which is not necessarily true.

If one considers the fit of this curve up to a point where $x = x_F$, $x_F > 2\gamma$ then:

(1) The number of ships

$$= \int_0^{2\gamma} \left(2\alpha x - \frac{2\alpha\gamma}{\pi} \sin \frac{\pi x}{\gamma} \right) dx + \int_{2\gamma}^{x_F} 2\alpha x \, dx = \alpha x_F^2, \quad \text{and}$$

(2) The mean distance of the annular distribution of ships about the central ship

$$= \frac{1}{\alpha x_F^2} \left[\int_0^{2\gamma} \left(2\alpha x^2 - \frac{2\alpha\gamma}{\pi} x \sin \frac{\pi x}{\gamma} \right) dx + \int_{2\gamma}^{x_F} 2\alpha x^2 \, dx \right]$$

$$= \frac{1}{\alpha x_F^2} \left[\frac{2\alpha x_F^3}{3} + \frac{4\alpha\gamma^3}{\pi^2} \right].$$

By equating observed and expected means we can obtain an estimate, $\hat{\gamma}$, of γ, thus:

$$\bar{x}. = \frac{2x_F}{3} + \frac{4\hat{\gamma}^3}{\pi^2} \cdot \frac{1}{x_F^2} \quad \text{giving} \quad \hat{\gamma}^3 = \left(\bar{x} x_F^2 - \frac{2}{3} x_F^3 \right) \pi^2 / 4 \quad .$$

However the data were in many cases too poor to give satisfactory results, particularly when there was a large fall-off in data beyond the domain boundary.

3. Method of displaced numbers

This is the most satisfactory method so far developed. It makes no assumptions on what the resulting displacements look like but uses the fact that once point C is reached (Fig. 5) the total number of ships in any area defined by $x < x_c$ will equal the total number of ships to be expected in the area given uniform density.

Let y_i be the total number of ships observed in the ith annulus from the centre with outside radius x_i and mean radius $m_i = \frac{1}{2}(x_{i+1} + x_i)$.

Let e_i be the smoothed number of ships observed in the ith annulus where

$$e_i = \frac{1}{3}\left(y_{i-1} + y_i + y_{i+1}\right), \text{ as before.}$$

If $y = 2\alpha x$ is the line for uniform density in the annular distribution of ships, then the total number of ships expected in the total area of outer width x_i is $\alpha x_i^2 = T_i$.

Number of ships expected in annulus

$$= \int_{x_{i-1}}^{x_i} 2\alpha x dx = \alpha\left(x_i - x_{i-1}\right)2m_i = \frac{\alpha m_i}{5},$$

if all annuli have an equal width of $\frac{1}{10}$ n mile.

An estimate of α is therefore given by $\frac{\hat{\alpha}m_i}{5} = e_i$ and so $\hat{T}_i = \frac{5e_i}{m_i} x_i^2$ gives an estimate for T_i.

We now let $C_i = \overset{i}{\underset{k=1}{\Sigma}} e_k$ be the smoothed total of ships observed in the area of outer width x_i, and set $\hat{T}_i - C_i = \delta_i$. For $x < x_c$ we would expect δ_i to be positive since the total number of ships in this region is decreased by the displacement process. For $x \geqslant x_c$, we would expect δ_i to change sign at random, because of random fluctuations around the uniform density line in this area.

E

Hence the value of x_c may be found by estimating
where δ_i has ceased to be consistently of one sign, ignoring
fluctuations at small values of x_i where small numbers of shi
are involved. One or two ships very close to the central shi
can distort the pattern and hence fluctuations of less than
ten ships were ignored. Temporary fluctuations of one value
were also ignored. To find x_A, the domange, a graph of the
values for the smoothed numbers of ships is plotted; by joini
(x_c, e_c) to the origin the line of uniform density is obtainec
the point of intersection of this line and the plotted curve
of observed values is the point A. An illustration of this
method is given in Table 2 and Fig. 9.

Table 2

Calculation of the domain boundary by the method of displacec
numbers sunk data: Survey 3   Sector 3

x_i $\frac{1}{10}$ n miles	sign of $\delta_i =$ $T_i - C_i$	x_i $\frac{1}{10}$ n miles	sign o $\delta_i =$ $T_i - C_i$
1		14	−
2	+	15	−
3	+	16	−
4	+	17	+
5	+	18	+
6	+	19	−
7	+	20	−
8	+	21	−
9	+	22	−
10	−*	23	−
11	−	24	−
12	+	25	−
13	+	26	−

*$(x_c, e_c) = (0.95, 8.3)$ point C

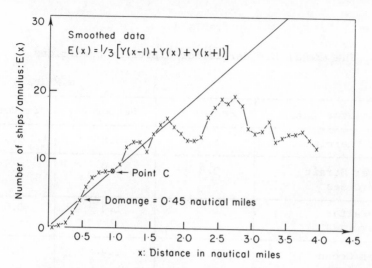

Fig. 9   Sunk survey data: Survey 3: Sector 3: Evaluation of
the domange

It is felt that this is the most satisfactory method
developed so far as it takes into account the behaviour of the
ships under the displacement hypothesis. Because it is based
on an objective principle it is superior to a purely graphical
approach. Its advantages over a curve fitting method are that
it will yield results even with poor data and it is unnecessary
to make further assumptions about the form of displacement
curve. There are however still some disadvantages, the main
being that in some cases there is still a degree of subjecti-
vity left both in the choice of point C and point A. Secondly
the method was not completely computerised since the final
determination by graphical methods had to be done by hand.
Thus it is realised that the method is by no means ideal but
it does provide results which for the most part seem reasonably
realistic. Table 3 shows a summary of results obtained under
different conditions, which are considered generally to be of
the right order for the different navigational areas. For instance one would expect much higher values in the Open Ocean
where there is considerable freedom to manoeuvre than in the
Dover Strait where the amount of navigable water is severely
restricted and there are many more ships around. It also seems
reasonable that the values for the Dover Strait in poor visibility should be similar to those for the southern North Sea
in good visibility.

Table 3

The domain boundaries for different conditions

N.Miles

A:

Simulator Data	Sector 1	Sector 2	Sector 3
All Exercises	1.3	0.8	0.5
Dover Strait Exercises	0.8	0.8	0.1
Gibraltar Exercises	1.5	1.4	0.6
Open Ocean Exercises	2.4	2.4	0.9

B:

Sunk Survey Data	Sector 1	Sector 2	Sector 3
All Surveys	0.9	0.7	0.5
Survey 1	0.5	0.5	0.4
Survey 2	0.9	0.9	0.8
Survey 3	0.7	0.6	0.5

A: Simulator Data by Sector and by type of Area.

B: Sunk Data by Sector and by Survey.

HYPOTHESIS TESTS FOR THE PRESENCE OF A DOMAIN

Once a line of uniform density has been established tests can be made to see if the hypothesis of the presence of a domain is substantiated. Therefore it is required to test the null hypothesis.

H_0: no domain exists and the underlying pattern is one of uniform density
against the alternative hypothesis

H_1: a domain exists.

A maximum significance level of 5% is considered appropriate. If uniform density exists then one would expect the points to be roughly in equal numbers on either side of the line of uniform density. However if a domain exists then in theory for $x < x_A$ (domange) the points will all lie below the line and for $x_A < x < x_c$ (end of displacement) the points will all be above the line as in Fig. 5. Thus for $x < x_c$ the number of points in the direction of the domain and against it can be counted. Under H_0 if the points are randomly scattered about the line then each point has an equal chance of being in the direction of the domain or against it. Thus if Z is a random variable denoting the number of points out of n in the direction of the domain, Z has a binomial distribution with parameters n and $\frac{1}{2}$. Hence if z is the observed value of Z, any situation for which the probability $(Z < z | H_0$ is true) < 0.05 can be considered to be significant. Table 4 shows a summary of the results of this test and it can be seen that of 24 results only one is non-significant, namely the Dover Strait exercises, Sector 3. Ideally one would like to test the values for $x > x_c$ to see if they are significantly different from uniform density, but this is not practical because of the fall off in data.

STANDARD ERRORS OF THE DOMAIN BOUNDARIES

Since these are obviously sample results, they provide only estimates of the size of the domain boundary. It would thus be useful if confidence limits could be established for the population results. As only limited data were available the only feasible approach was to make an assumption about the form of the underlying distribution of displacements in the presence of the domain. If it is assumed that n ships are displaced and the underlying distribution is normal, then confidence intervals for x_A, the domange, are given by:

$$\hat{x}_A \pm z_\alpha \frac{\hat{\sigma}}{\sqrt{n}}$$

where $\hat{x}_A$ is the estimated value of x_A from the sample results,

$\hat{\sigma}^2$ is the estimated variance among the ships which are displaced, and

z_α is the probability factor derived from standard normal tables or from t - tables if the sample is small.

Table 4

Results of hypothesis tests on the presence of a domain:
simulator data and sunk survey data by sector and by type
of sea area

	No. of Values in the Direction of the Domain	No. of Values against the Domain	Total No. of Values	Probability
	SIMULATOR DATA: ALL EXERCISES			
Sector 1	18	4	22	.0022
Sector 2	26	1	27	.0000
Sector 3	8	1	9	.0195
DOVER STRAIT				
Sector 1	14	1	15	.0005
Sector 2	11	0	11	.0005
Sector 3	4	0	4	.0625*
GIBRALTAR				
Sector 1	21	1	22	.0000
Sector 2	23	2	25	.0000
Sector 3	10	0	10	.0010
OPEN OCEAN				
Sector 1	38	0	38	.0000
Sector 2	37	3	40	.0000
Sector 3	11	2	13	.0112
SUNK SURVEY DATA				
Sector 1	14	2	16	.0021
Sector 2	10	3	13	0.461
Sector 3	19	0	19	.0000

σ^2 was calculated using all ships within a distance $0 \leqslant x \leqslant x_c$.
This is strictly not correct as many of the ships in this area
so defined are not involved in the displacement process. However this probably overestimates σ which is wisest given the
other sources of error. n is calculated using the formula:

$$n = C_c \frac{x_A^2}{x_c^2}$$

where C_c is the cumulative total of ships in the area defined
by $0 \leqslant x \leqslant x_c$ and x_A and x_c are defined as before. Table 5
gives a summary of the values of the standard errors, $\hat{\sigma}/\sqrt{\hat{n}}$,
found by this method together with the domain boundaries. For
95% confidence intervals, when the sample is large $z_\alpha = 1.96 \simeq 2$.
Thus an interval of 2 × standard error around the value of
the domain boundary quoted gives some estimate of the expected
variability. Again the result of the Dover Strait exercises,
Sector 3 stands out as the only non-realistic result. Although
it is felt that considerable reliance cannot be put on these
standard errors because of the many assumptions involved,
they do at least provide an approximation to the degree of
variability.

USES OF SHIP DOMAINS

1. *Encounter Rates*

The effectiveness of traffic schemes can be assessed
objectively by considering encounter rates. It is suggested
that the ship domain should define the encounter area; an encounter can be said to have occurred if one ship would have
entered the domain of another had no avoiding action been
taken. For analytical investigations it is often desirable
to take a simple geometrical model as an approximation to a
domain; the most suitable which has been found so far is an
ellipse with major axis inclined to the direction of the ship's
head.

2. *Computer simulation models*

The findings on ship domains provide a suitable basis from
which computer simulation models can be built. As each ship
enters the system data could be attached to it relating the
required domain dimensions to the size of the ship and giving

Table 5

The standard errors of the domain boundary in nautical miles under different conditions

N. Miles

Simulator Data	SECTOR 1		SECTOR 2		SECTOR 3	
	Domain Boundary	Standard Error	Domain Boundary	Standard Error	Domain Boundary	Standard Error
All Exercises	1.33	.056	0.78	.093	0.45	.062
Dover Strait	0.82	.078	0.77	.061	0.10	.207
Gibraltar	1.49	.059	1.40	.064	0.57	.078
Open Ocean	2.35	.049	2.35	.080	0.85	.122

A: Simulator data by sector and by type of sea area

Table 5 (Cont.)

N. Miles

Sunk Data	SECTOR 1		SECTOR 2		SECTOR 3	
	Domain Boundary	Standard Error	Domain Boundary	Standard Error	Domain Boundary	Standard Error
All Surveys	0.85	.045	0.70	.045	0.45	.055
Survey 1	0.47	.062	0.50	.072	0.35	.043
Survey 2	0.87	.072	0.91	.063	0.78	.057
Survey 3	0.71	.088	0.58	.069	0.45	.031

B: Sunk data by sector and by survey

details on the adaptation of the domain to changes in relative
velocity and density. The passage of the ship through the are
would be done with the dual objectives of reaching the planned
destination and maintaining a clear domain. Thus, before each
move, all possible courses of action could be evaluated and
the optimum chosen. The presence of several ships in the area
will mean that it will not always be possible to maintain a
clear domain and hence encounters will occur from time to
time. Once a realistic computer simulation is built for an
area, there are a variety of problems to which it may be appli

3. External over-all control of sea traffic

Many discussions have been held in recent years on the extent to which marine traffic should be subjected to external
control. The first steps towards the establishment of marine
traffic control systems outside terminal areas and port
approaches have already been taken with mandatory routeing
systems in the Dover Strait and elsewhere. One extension of
this could be the setting up of shore based stations which
would guide a ship through a congested area according to agree
separation standards for which ship domain dimensions could
provide a basis. A common set of standards could be used for
all ships or they could be varied according to the size of
ship. They could also take into account the accuracy of navigation and be such that the probability of collision was below
a certain level. For practical reasons it might be impossible
to control all ships in an area in this way and the service
could be restricted to certain types such as large tankers.
Instead of shore based guidance for the whole passage through
an area, control could be set over the number of ships entering an area, since the presence of a large number of ships
could lead to the compression of domain boundaries below a
level which was considered acceptable.

4. Traffic flows

A basic equation in any traffic engineering study is that
of traffic flow: Volume = Density × Speed. From this equation
it is possible to define the basic capacity of a channel which
may be thought of as the maximum number of ships that can
negotiate the channel in a given unit of time assuming normal
navigating conditions and ships of similar types. A knowledge
of ship domains enables these basic capacities to be calculate

CONCLUSIONS

    The concept of a ship domain has been developed and a
brief outline of some of its applications has been given.
However the main purpose of this paper has been to discuss
the methods used to evaluate the dimensions of a domain. More
work needs to be done on the methods of analysing the data.
For instance, a further investigation of suitable analytical
models for the distribution of ships around the central ship
would be valuable. If an algebraic model could be developed
for the domain then many of the marine applications such as
encounter rates and traffic capacity could be investigated
further analytically. Fig. 10 shows an actual domain found
for the southern North Sea.

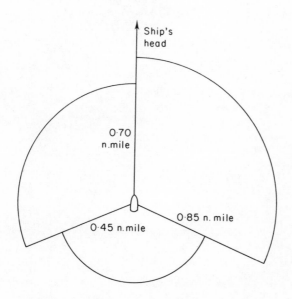

Fig. 10   A ship domain for the Sunk Area of the North Sea

REFERENCES

Fujii, Y. and Tanaka, K. (1971) "Traffic capacity", *J. of
Nav.*, **24**, 543.

Goodwin, E. and Kemp, J. (1977) "A Survey of Marine Traffic in
the southern North Sea, *J. of Nav.*, **30**, 378.

THE MODELLING OF MARINE TRAFFIC FLOW AND POTENTIAL ENCOUNTERS*

G.R.G. Lewison

(National Maritime Institute)

1. INTRODUCTION

If two ships are moving in an area of sea, they will be
able to keep their courses unless one or both of the mariners
controlling them considers that they would make too close an
approach. In these circumstances it is necessary for some
avoiding action to be taken, usually a change of course by one
ship. The Collision Regulations are an attempt to define the
circumstances in which action is necessary, and to specify
what should be done and by whom. Such an event in the passage
of a ship may be called an "encounter". Most such encounters
are satisfactorily resolved, but a few are not and lead either
to a near miss, or perhaps a collision. Barratt (p.161) has
explored the relation between these two types of event. Other
writers, notably Fujii and Shiobara (1971), have examined the
relationship between the number of encounters and the number
of collisions which they call the "chance of mismanoeuvre".
I have also examined this question (1978). Here we derive
means of estimating the numbers of ship encounters and examine
how they depend upon the characteristics of the marine traffic.

The word "encounter" requires more precise definition.
There are four possible ways in which the term may be used.
The first meaning is that implied above, that is, an actual
situation in which, if no avoiding action were taken, two
ships would have a closest point of approach within a given
distance, say half a mile. (This is assumed to be accurately
determined by the mariners. In practice, of course, the instruments used to measure the other ship's relative track will
have errors. Thus in some instances the mariner may not rea-
lise that the miss distance is as close as half a mile, or
conversely he may think that a situation would lead to an encounter whereas in fact the ships would pass well clear). If
all the tracks and speeds of ships in an area of sea are known,
then the threatened miss distances between each pair of ships

*©IMA: Controller HMSO London, 1979

can be calculated, and those less than the critical distance
counted. This distance is called the "encounter radius". It
is necessary to set some minimum time over which the ship
tracks (determined, presumably, by radar) should be averaged
in order to exclude spurious encounters. This particular
exercise has not been carried out, so far as I am aware.

The second meaning, normally used by marine traffic engineers, is an actual situation when two ships are within a
given distance of each other. Barratt and Hewson (1974) coun
a number of such encounters in the Dover Strait by noting whe
the radar echoes of two ships merged. They estimated that
this represented a mutual approach within half a mile. Coupa
in France has produced computer-plotted maps, based on auto-
mated analysis of radar photographs taken at Cap Gris Nez,
which also show the number, type and location of encounters.

The third definition, and the one used here, is akin to
the first, but is based not upon observations of real ships
but on a mathematical model. The input to the model is a description of the various components of the total traffic flow,
their density, speed and distribution across a line. The output is the number of encounters of different types. This
should be the same as the number observed on the first definition provided that the description of the traffic flow is
sufficiently detailed for the model to be accurate, and that
the real-life observation is made over a long enough time to
make sampling errors negligible. It will however be greater
than the number observed on the second definition (i.e., actu
approaches) because mariners generally take avoidance action
early in order to prevent a close-quarter situation from developing.

The fourth definition is a meeting situation between two
ships that causes one or both to take significant avoiding
action. It applies to real situations, and would generally
include those encounters on the first definition that are subsequently excluded by the second definition (i.e., those occa
sions when ships increase the threatened miss distance from
below half a mile to above it). It would also include some
situations not covered by the first definition (i.e., when
an alteration of course takes place even though the threatene
miss distance never fell below half a mile), and also, to jud
by the reports of some collisions, some falling within the
second definition and not the first (i.e., in which the miss
distance was decreased as a result of avoidance manoeuvres).
Its practical importance lies in the way it may be used to

describe mariners' behaviour. The "radius of encounter" will
not be fixed, but will depend on such parameters as visibility,
ship manoeuvring characteristics, and the direction of the
threat.

In this paper, some methods of modifying the counting
method based on the mathematical model to take account of
mariners' behaviour in real situations will be discussed.
These take the form of allowing the radius of encounter to vary
with direction. However it is generally premature to advance
far along this road until more evidence is available about
the readiness with which mariners will take action to avoid
collisions.

The estimation of numbers of encounters from shipping movements is a useful exercise because it allows marine traffic
management to be more soundly based. A proposal to alter the
way in which ships navigate in a particular area can be examined, and judged, on the basis of whether more or fewer encounters would result. A rather obvious example is the one-way
movement of traffic in separation schemes, which can largely
eliminate head-on encounters. However the concentration of
each half of the traffic flow into half the width of passage
tends to increase the number of overtaking encounters, as we
shall see. The mathematical model allows relatively precise
estimates to be made of the effect of changes in traffic management. If estimates are also available of the risk of each encounter leading to a collision, then the effect of such changes
on the accident rate may be predicted. This will then allow
rational decisions to be made on whether proposed management
schemes are likely to be cost-effective.

2. THE MATHEMATICAL ENCOUNTER MODEL

2.1 *General description: circular encounter area*

We consider a rectangular area of sea of length L and
width W (Fig. 1). There is a flow of ships of differing speeds
across the boundary EF in the direction FG, which is described
by the flow rate S_A (ships per unit of gatewidth and per unit of
time). Each ship is assumed to travel across the area with a
constant speed v_A, but the number of ships in each speed range
v_A to $v_A + \delta v_A$ varies, and is given by $S_A . f_A (v_A) \delta v_A$ where the
function $f_A (v_A)$ satisfies

$$\int_0^\infty f_A(v_A) \cdot dv_A = 1 \tag{1}$$

but is not otherwise limited.

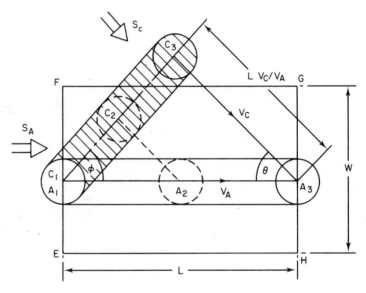

Fig. 1   Diagram showing area for analysis of crossing ship C
coming into encounter with mainstream ship A.

As a result of the traffic, there will be a certain density
of shipping in the area, which can be measured by a density
function ρ_A, also a function of speed. By continuity, we have

$$\rho_A(v_A) \cdot v_A \cdot \delta v_A = S_A \cdot f_A(v_A) \cdot \delta v_A \quad \text{giving} \tag{2}$$

$$\rho_A(v_A) = S_A \cdot f_A(v_A)/v_A \quad \text{and}$$

$$\int_0^\infty \rho_A(v_A) \cdot dv_A = D_A = S_A \int_0^\infty \left\{ f_A(v_A)/v_A \right\} \cdot dv_A \tag{3}$$

where D_A is the over-all average ship density, (ships per unit area).

There is also assumed to be a second stream of marine traffic proceeding at an angle θ to the first stream, and characterised by suffix C. At any given time, there will be a certain density of crossing traffic, D_C, and a ship of the first stream will encounter such ships if they are within a certain radius, which may be called the "encounter radius". We mentioned above that the concept of encounter could be treated both theoretically (with a fixed radius) and on the basis of observation of mariners' reactions. In this section we assume that the radius is fixed, and proceed to calculate the number of encounters.

The "encounter radius", traced out around a ship in the different directions from which threats may come, will effectively generate an "encounter area". This is shown as circular in Fig. 1, but can in principle be of any shape. It may be compared with what Fujii and Shiobara (1970) and Goodwin (1975) have called a "domain", which is the area round a vessel that she is observed to keep free of other traffic. However, there is an important distinction. The "domain" is estimated in terms of the actual density of shipping observed to occur around a vessel, whereas the "encounter area" is the desired area which the vessel would try to keep clear. In particular, we may note that a crossing vessel (C) approaching from the starboard side would, according to the Collision Regulations, be the stand-on vessel if a collision were threatened, and the other vessel (A) would therefore be expected to give way. The "encounter radius" would therefore be determined by A. If C were crossing from A's port side, she would be expected to give way, and therefore to determine the encounter radius. Only if A feared that C would not, or could not, give way would she take action herself. In theory, if A and C were similar ships, one would expect the encounter area for A to be symmetrical port and starboard. However in any real marine traffic situation, the crossing traffic may well be different from the main stream traffic, and the encounter area will take the form of an irregular figure, not symmetrical about the fore-and-aft direction. Both Fujii and Goodwin have suggested that the "domain" may be elliptical, and in the following section an elliptical encounter area has been included as a variant on the basic circular shape. Other shapes could be used if desired.

We may say that a ship, A, will come into encounter with a crossing vessel, C, if in A's passage from A_1 to A_3 there exists a ship which is initially outside A's "encounter area" and at some later time, say when A is at A_2, is inside the area (dotted in Fig. 1). The encounter will be said to take place when C crosses the boundary of A's encounter area. We are interested in the number of such ships C that may come into encounter with A during A's passage of length L from A_1 to A_3. We construct the position C_3 such that any ship C starting from C_3 when A is at A_1 would just reach A_3 at the same instant as A. (The ships for the purposes of this analysis are regarded as small, and it is assumed that no alteration of course take place.) Then any ship C that was initially in the encounter area equal and similarly oriented to that of A and centred about C_3 would subsequently be in actual encounter with A when the latter was at A_3. Similar arguments hold for the encounter area centred at C_2: ships C initially there would have reached the encounter area centred at A_2 when A was there. Thus we conclude that a ship C would come into encounter with A if C were in the shaded area in Fig. 1 when A was at A_1. This area excludes the encounter area about A_1 but includes that about C_3. It is equal in area to that of a rectangle of length A_1C_3 and breadth the projection of the encounter area onto a line perpendicular to A_1C_3. Let this area be M. Then the number of ships C of velocity v_C to $v_C + \delta v_C$ in this area will be

$$M.\rho_C(v_C).\delta v_C = M.S_C.(f_C(v_C)/v_C)\ \delta v_C \qquad (4)$$

which will be the number of encounters by A in a passage of length L, that is, during time L/v_A. So the encounter rate, N, per unit time for A will be

$$N = (M/L).S_C.v_A/v_C.f_C(v_C).\delta v_C \ . \qquad (5)$$

It remains to calculate M. If the encounter area is circular, and of radius r, then $M = A_1C_3.2r$, and

$$M/L = 2r.\{1+(v_C/v_A)^2-2(v_C/v_A).\cos\theta\}^{0.5} \qquad (6)$$

and so

$$N = 2r.S_C.\{1+(v_A/v_C)^2-2(v_A/v_C).\cos\theta\}^{0.5}. \qquad (7)$$

This expression is based on a traffic flow measured across a line perpendicular to its direction of motion, as shown in Fig. 1. However, it is often more useful to measure the crossing flow across a line parallel to the mainstream traffic. If S_C' is such a flow, then S_C in (7), and also in (15), must be replaced by $S_C'/\sin\theta$.

2.2 Elliptical encounter area

If the encounter area is elliptical, with major and minor semi-diameters p and q, and with the major axis offset an angle α to starboard of A's direction of travel (Fig. 2) then the shaded area M will equal the length A_1C_3 multiplied by

$BB'\sin(\beta+\phi)$, where the boundaries of the shaded area are tangential to the ellipse at B and B'. As before,

$$A_1C_3 = L\{1+(v_C/v_A)^2-2(v_C/v_A).\cos\theta\}^{0.5} \qquad (8)$$

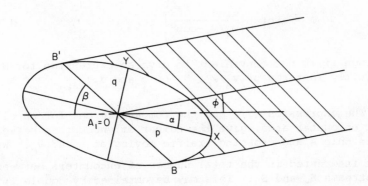

Fig. 2   Diagram showing the geometry of an elliptical encounter
         area

The tangents to the ellipse have slope (relative to axes OXY) $\tan(\alpha+\phi)$. The equation to the ellipse in this sytem of coordinates is

$$(x/p)^2+(y/q)^2 = 1 \qquad (9)$$

and at B and B',

$$\frac{dy}{dx} = \frac{-x_B}{y_B} \cdot \frac{q^2}{p^2} = \tan(\alpha+\phi) \quad . \tag{10}$$

Hence, from equations (9) and (10), we have

$$x_B^2 = \frac{p^4}{p^2} \frac{\tan^2(\alpha+\phi)}{\tan^2(\alpha+\phi)+q^2} \tag{11}$$

$$y_B^2 = \frac{q^4}{p^2} \frac{1}{\tan^2(\alpha+\phi)+q^2} \quad .$$

Now

$$\frac{y_B}{x_B} = \tan(\beta-\alpha) = \frac{q^2}{p^2} \frac{1}{\tan(\alpha+\phi)} \tag{12}$$

and

$$BB' = 2\left(x_B^2+y_B^2\right)^{0.5} = 2\left\{\frac{p^4}{p^2} \frac{\tan^2(\alpha+\phi)+q^4}{\tan^2(\alpha+\phi)+q^2}\right\}^{0.5} . \tag{13}$$

The value of BB'tan$(\beta+\phi)$ can now be found since

$$\phi = \arctan\left\{\frac{\sin\theta}{v_A/v_C-\cos\theta}\right\} \tag{14}$$

although it is not convenient to give an expression for N explicitly in terms of v_A/v_C, θ, p, q and α.

The expression (7), and the comparable one for an elliptical encounter area, give the number of encounters between a single ship A and crossing traffic moving at speed v_C. We are often interested in the total number of encounters between the streams S_A and S_C. This may be obtained by double integration, and we have, for the number of encounters per unit area and per unit time,

$$N(S_A,S_C) = S_A S_C \int_0^\infty f_C(v_C)\,dv_C \int_0^\infty \frac{f_A(v_A)}{v_A} \cdot 2r\left\{1+(v_A/v_C)^2-2(v_C/v_A)\cos\theta\right\}$$

where r = the effective encounter radius which may not necessarily be constant. We have here considered the possible variation of r with angle of encounter; it is also possible that it is a function of ship type and speed.

2.3 Head-on and overtaking encounters

The encounters discussed so far are all of the crossing type, although some of those occurring with small angles of θ might be classified as "overtaking" under the Collision Regulations. We turn now to the very important class of encounters between ships of the main stream, A. These will be of the overtaking type, or, if rogues are present which are travelling counter to the main flow direction, of head-on type.

There arises immediately a qualification: we need to know the way the traffic in the stream is distributed laterally. Equation (15) holds for <u>any</u> distribution of traffic in the main stream and the crossing stream, provided only that the area in which the encounters are being counted is large enough to cover the area crossed by both streams.

To calculate the number of head-on and overtaking encounters we shall assume initially that the lateral distribution of traffic is uniform, and then make a correction for the effect of lateral bunching. For overtaking encounters in stream A, we introduce the dummy variable $v_{A'}$ and write

$$N_O(S_A) = S_A^2 \int_0^\infty f_A(v_A)\,dv_A \int_0^\infty f_{A'}(v_{A'})\,dv_{A'}\cdot 2r\{\mathrm{mod}\,(1/v_A - 1/v_{A'})\} \quad (16)$$

since $\cos\theta$ is unity. For head-on encounters between stream A and the rogues B,

$$N_H(S_A, S_B) = S_A \cdot S_B \int_0^\infty f_A(v_A)\,dv_A \int_0^\infty f_B(v_B)\,dv_B \cdot 2r \cdot (1/v_A + 1/v_B) \quad (17)$$

since $\cos\theta = -1$.

We now consider the situation where the flow is not uniform across reference lines drawn perpendicular to the flow. If all "gates" have ships with similar speed distributions $f_A(v_A)$, but the rate of flow is given by $g_A(y)\delta y$ in each

infinitesimal gate of width δy, then we may define a mean flo
$p_A(y_A)$ at any point such that

$$p_A(y_A) = \int_{y_A-r}^{y_A+r} (g_A(y)/S_A.2r)\,dy \qquad (18)$$

where $p_A(y_A)$ is normalised with respect to the mean flow S_A.
Then the over-all proportion of ships that are theoretically
able to encounter each other is therefore

$$\left.\begin{array}{l} (1/W) \displaystyle\int_0^W p_A^2(y)\,dy = n(A,A) \\[3em] (1/W) \displaystyle\int_0^W p_A(y)p_B(y)\,dy = n(A,B) \end{array}\right\} \qquad (19)$$

or

where n is a multiplicatory factor to be introduced into the
right hand sides of equations (16) and (17) to compensate for
the non-uniformity of flow. (It has been tacitly assumed tha
the distribution of traffic is a continuous function in y beyond y = 0 and y = W and that values of $g_A(y)$ are available
over the range $-r \leqslant y \leqslant W+r$.) In practice, n>1 and some actual
numerical values are given in section 3.6.

3.   NUMERICAL RESULTS FOR TRAFFIC IN THE DOVER STRAIT

3.1 Description of the traffic

    The theoretical results given above could be applied to
any traffic situation, but it is convenient to illustrate some
of the conclusions by using velocity distributions derived
from actual observation. For some years, the NMI has been
observing traffic flow in the Dover Strait, and there now exis
a substantial body of data on this traffic system. The speed
distribution $f_A(v_A)$ has been taken from Fig. 5 of the report
by Cash and Boribond (1973), which refers to ships on "throug|
voyages" in the main lanes of the Dover Strait during a perioc
of 3 days of good visibility in May 1972.

Table I gives the speed distribution in terms of the numbers of ships observed within ±0.5 knot of certain speeds.

Table I

Speed, k	1	2	3	4	5	6	7	8
No. of ships	0	0	1	1	6	13	17	23
Speed, k	9	10	11	12	13	14	15	16
No. of ships	46	38	38	52	30	30	21	16
Speed, k	17	18	19	20	21	22	23	24
No. of ships	14	17	13	5	2	1	0	1

This distribution is plotted as a cumulative exceedance curve in Fig. 3. It has a mean of 11.98 knots and a standard deviation of 3.68 knots.

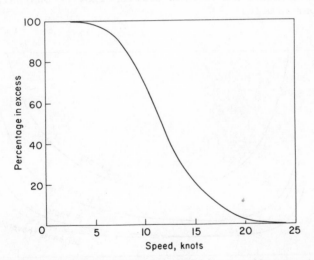

Fig. 3 Cumulative distribution of speed for through traffic in main lanes of Dover Strait (May 1972)

Crossing traffic in the Channel consists mainly of ferries (speed about 18 knots) and hovercraft (speed about 50 knots), but we can calculate the number of encounters for crossing traffic at any speed. The calculations are performed for unit flow rate in each stream, that is one ship per n.mile lane width per hour, and give the expected number of encounters per square n.mile per hour between traffic having the speed

distribution given in the above table and crossing traffic of
uniform speed. The numbers of encounters with crossing traffi
of a given speed distribution may be calculated by partitionir
it into separate speed groups and adding the respective encounter frequencies. (It is assumed in the model that traffic
is sufficiently light that the encounters take place singly,
and are independent of one another.

3.2 Crossing traffic: circular encounter area

The results of the calculations are given in Figs. 4 to 7
The ordinate scale in Figs. 4 and 5 is the number of encounter
per sq.n.mile and per hour if the flow rates for each stream
are one ship per hour and per n.mile perpendicular to the flow
direction. For the crossing traffic the streamwidth is actual
immaterial, and the ordinate gives the number of encounters
per n.mile width of mainstream for each crossing ship, on the
assumption that the mainstream traffic flow is one ship per
hour and per n.mile.

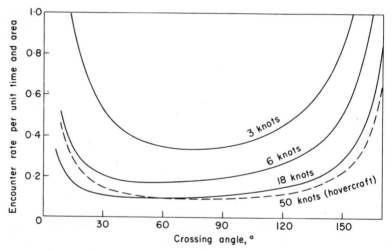

Fig. 4 Encounter frequency for vessels crossing Dover Strait
         main lanes. Circular area, diameter 1 n.mile

Figs. 4 and 5 show (at different scales) the encounter
frequencies for a range of speeds of the crossing ship from
3 knots (typical of trawlers when fishing) to 50 knots (hovercraft), and for a circular area of encounter. The crossing
angle giving the smallest number of encounters varies with the

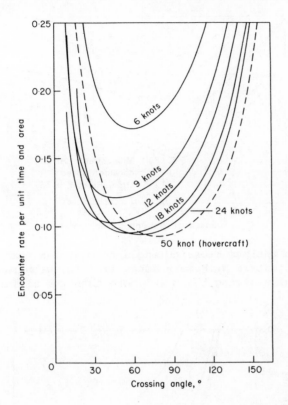

Fig. 5   Encounter frequency for vessels crossing Dover Strait
         main lanes.   Circular area, diameter 1 n.mile

speed of the crossing traffic as shown in Fig. 6, which also
indicates the rather wide spread of crossing angles possible
without significant increase in this number.   (Also shown is
the result obtained earlier by Barratt (1973) who considered
the case of main stream traffic travelling at uniform speed).

Over quite a range of speeds, a crossing at 50° is better
than one at 90°; the reduction in encounter frequency is 18%
for 12 knots and 12% for 18 knots crossing traffic.   But this
improvement only occurs if a ship, when crossing two opposing
traffic streams in succession, makes a smart 80° turn at the
lane separation boundary.   Such a manoeuvre might be rather
confusing for mainstream traffic near this boundary, and as
Fig. 7 shows, if no turn is made, a crossing at 90° is best
for all speeds.   The IMCO recommends that crossings of two main
lanes in succession should be made at a right angle or as close

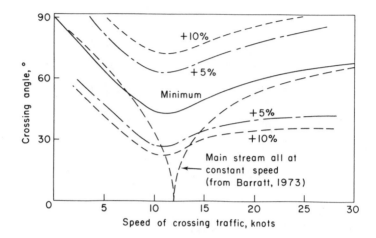

Fig. 6   The optimum crossing angle to minimise numbers of
encounters with main lanes traffic, with range of
angles giving 5 and 10% more than the minimum

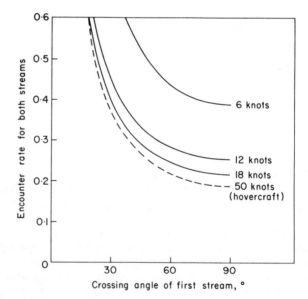

Fig. 7   Encounter rate if two opposing main lanes are crossed
without change of course

as practicable thereto, and Fig. 7 shows that this is good
advice.

3.3 Crossing traffic: elliptical encounter area

The effect of changing the shape of the area of encounter
(while keeping its total area constant) upon the number of encounters is shown in Figs. 8 and 9 for one speed of crossing
traffic, namely 18 knots. For an elliptical encounter area
with its axis aligned with the ship, the increase in eccentricity makes the encounter frequency curve flatter. Not surprisingly, the main stream ship presents a larger "target" for
crossing traffic and the number of encounters is increased.
If the encounter area is elliptical and has its axis offset,
Fig. 9 shows that very large differences can occur in encounter
numbers according to whether the axis is offset to starboard
(α positive) or to port (α negative) for crossing traffic
assumed approaching from port. (In this instance, the main
stream traffic would normally stand-on and the crossing traffic
would give way).

This suggests that examination of the behaviour of ships
in crossing situations might reveal the shape and orientation
of their encounter areas. If there is a difference in the
frequency of encounter between mainstream traffic and crossing
traffic from the two sides, this can be interpreted as showing
that the desired encounter radius (as seen by the readiness
of mainstream traffic to manoeuvre in the face of traffic
approaching from starboard) differs from that thought sufficient by the crossing traffic. Such a difference is simply
represented graphically by a skewed encounter area.

3.4 Head-on and overtaking encounters

We now consider the number of encounters of the head-on
and overtaking types between ships in the main stream, some
of which may be travelling in the wrong direction (rogues).
The numbers are given by equations (16) and (17). For speed
distributions given by Table I they are as follows:

$$N_O = 0.0345\ S_A^{\ 2} \tag{21}$$

$$N_H = 0.18547\ S_A . S_B \tag{22}$$

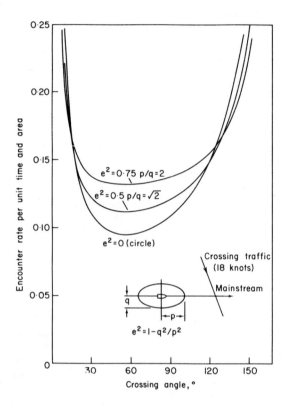

Fig. 8   The effect of eccentricity of an elliptical encounter
        area on encounter rate with mainstream traffic

The coefficients in these equations apply to a circular
encounter area of radius 0.5 n.mile. The effect of other
shapes and orientations of encounter areas is proportional to
their projection on to a line perpendicular to that of the
traffic flow. For small offset angles (below 25°) the encoun
cross-section decreases with increasing eccentricity and reac
only 71% of that of a circle for a 2:1 ellipse (e^2 = 0.75)
aligned with the flow, see Fig. 10.

For a traffic stream of total flow S_T partitioned into
a proportion 1-k (k<0.5) travelling in one direction and a
proportion, k, of rogues, we can write

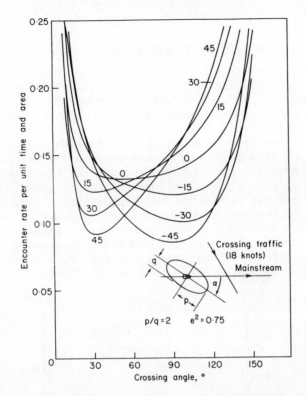

Fig. 9 The effect of skew of an elliptical encounter area
        (p/q = 2) on encounter rate with mainstream traffic

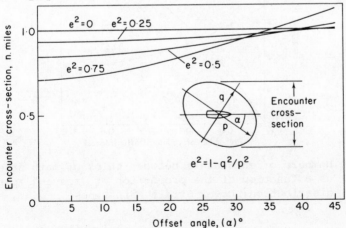

Fig. 10 Variation of encounter cross-section with offset angle
         for elliptical encounter areas (of equal area)

$$N_O = 0.0345 \ (k^2 + (1-k)^2).S_T^2$$

$$N_H = 0.18547 \ k(1-k).S_T^2 \qquad \qquad (23)$$

These functions are plotted in Fig. 11. The total number
of encounters is, as expected. a maximum when k = 0.5, that is
half the traffic is travelling in each direction, and a minimu
when k = 0 and all the ships are moving in the same direction
If there were an area of sea in which there were equal traffi
flows in each direction, and it was then split into two lanes
of equal width, one for each traffic stream, there would
(according to Fig. 11) be a reduction in the number of encoun
of 46%. There may be a more than proportionate reduction in
the number of collisions because of the elimination of the re
latively more dangerous head-on encounters. However it is
important to recognise that the number of overtaking encounte
will have doubled, and that these may then form a new source
of hazard for mariners. This is discussed by Curtis (p.175).

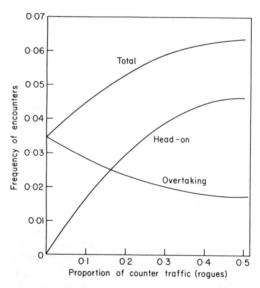

Fig. 11   Numbers of encounters between ships of main stream
          as a function of the proportion of "rogues". Speed
          distribution: Dover Strait Main Lanes

The numbers of head-on and overtaking encounters are equal when

$$0.18547 \ k(1-k) = 0.0345 \ (1-2k+2k^2) \qquad (24)$$

or k = 0.1617, i.e., just over 16% of the traffic is against the main flow direction. This result is in close agreement with that of Draper and Bennett (1973).

3.5 Effect of speed variability

It is of interest to examine the variation of numbers of encounters with the distribution of ship speeds. The effect of increasing the standard deviation has only a moderate effect on the numbers of head-on encounters (the mean speed remaining the same) but it greatly increases the number of overtaking encounters, as may be seen from Fig. 12. As more traffic separation schemes come into force, further reductions in the numbers of collisions, if they are to be achieved through a lowering of the encounter rate, will require some effort to reduce the variation between the speeds of ships in the same lane, for example by the imposition of a maximum and a minimum speed. If speeds could be controlled so that there were very few ships outside the range 8 to 16 knots (standard deviation = 2 knots, mean remaining at about 12 knots), then the number of overtaking encounters in the Dover Strait would be reduced by 50% from that occurring now. (This calculation assumes that the number of rogues is very small, which it is.)

Such measures may be difficult to achieve in practice. However in principle it would be possible to control the speed of an individual ship that was particularly hazardous because of the nature of her cargo. Figs. 13 and 14 show the expected numbers of overtaking encounters for a ship travelling in the main lanes at different speeds. Fig. 13 shows the variation of the encounter rate per unit time. As expected, the minimum rate occurs when the individual ship is travelling at the mean speed of the main stream. This result holds true for all speed distributions, including that measured in the main lanes of the Dover Strait (dashed curve). However when the numbers of encounters are divided by the vessel's speed to give the number per unit of distance travelled, which gives a measure of the risk attendant upon any particular passage (Fig. 14), a differ-ent pattern emerges. The speed giving the minimum encounter rate is now a function of the variability of mainstream traffic speeds; for Dover Strait traffic it is about 13.0 knots. If the standard deviation of the traffic could be halved, then so

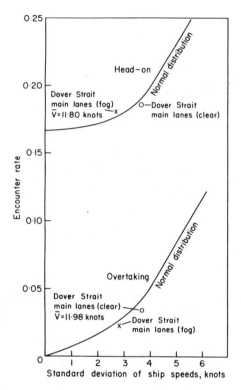

Fig. 12   Numbers of head-on and overtaking encounters between
          ships of mainstream(s) of mean speed 11.98 knots

could the numbers of overtaking encounters for a vessel travel
ling at the optimum speed. The latter is not especially
critical as the number of encounters varies rather little
with speed: over the range 11 to 30 knots the variation is
only 11%. (It should be noted that for slow ships the number
of encounters per unit of distance rises very steeply indeed.
If such ships travel in the main traffic lanes they will give
rise to large numbers of overtaking situations.)

3.6 Effect of lateral distribution

    At the end of section 2.3, formulae were given that allowe
a correction to be made to the numbers of head-on and overtaki
encounters in order to compensate for the non-uniformity of
traffic across the width of the area being studied. An exampl

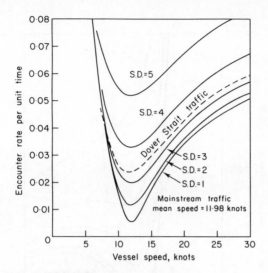

Fig. 13   Number of overtaking encounters for a vessel moving
with a traffic stream.   Time basis

of such a distribution is given by Barratt and Hewson (1974)
who presented histograms for flow rate in both clear and
foggy conditions in an area of the Dover Strait.   This area
was 4 n.miles wide and spanned part of the English Inshore
Zone and part of the Main Westbound Lane (Fig. 15).   Their
results for clear conditions are shown in Fig. 16.   The widths
of the bars have been scaled so that the mean flow in each
direction is taken as unity.   The actual mean flow rates across
the 4 mile wide gate are 0.89 ship per n.mile-hour westbound
and 0.118 ship per n.mile-hour eastbound.   The plot is therefore of $g_A(y).W/S_A$ and $g_B(y).W/S_B$.

From this plot it is possible to calculate the values of
$p_A(y)$ and $p_B(y)$ by averaging the values of Fig. 16 over ±0.5
n.mile.   The n factor (equation (19)) can now be determined
for head-on encounters if $p_A(y).p_B(y)$ is plotted and the mean
value taken.   This is done on the left side of Fig. 17, and
n(A,B) (or n_H) = 1.22.   This means that the number of head-on
encounters in the area is given by equation (22) as

N_H = 1.22 x 0.18547 x 0.89 x 0.118 per sq.n.mile-hour

= 0.57 per sq.n.mile-day

F

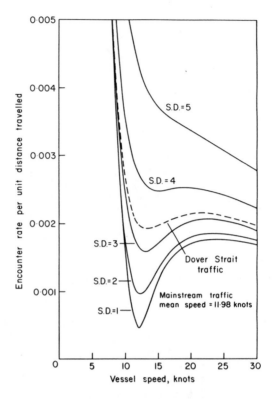

Fig. 14   Number of overtaking encounters for a vessel moving
           with a traffic stream.   Distance basis

on the assumption that the speed distribution of the ships was
the same as in Cash and Boribond's survey (1973).

For overtaking encounters the procedure is slightly more
complex as the encounters within each stream have to be treated
separately. It is therefore necessary to plot

$$(s_A^2 \cdot p_A(y) + s_B^2 \cdot p_B(y))/(s_A^2 + s_B^2)$$

in order to give a weighted average value of $n(A,A)$ and $n(B,B)$
which we may write n_0. The function is plotted on the right
side of Fig. 17, and we find that $n_0 = 1.24$. Therefore the
number of overtaking encounters in the area is given by

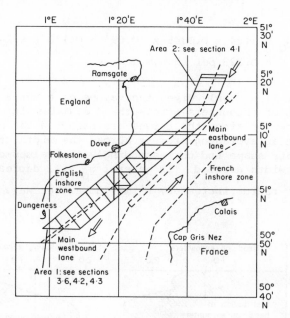

Fig. 15   Map of the Dover Strait, showing traffic separation
          zones and areas used for analysis by Barratt and
          Hewson (1974)

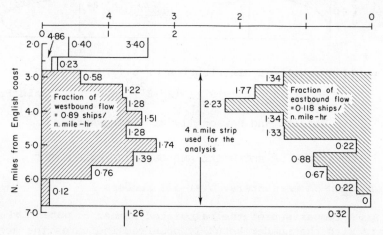

Fig. 16   Normalised traffic distributions in Dover Strait from
          Barratt and Hewson (1974). Clear weather; based on
          92 hours observations 3rd - 5th Nov. 1972 and 6th -
          7th Jan. 1973

equation (21) as

$$N_O = 1.24 \times 0.0345 \times (0.89^2 + 0.118^2) \times 24$$
$$= 0.828 \text{ per sq.n.mile-day.}$$

Fig. 17 not only gives the values of n but also the distribution of encounters across the 4 n. miles width of the stud
area. However since the curves are based on the p(y) which
depend on an averaging process across the width of the encount
area, their shape and correspondingly the values of n will va
with the width assumed. In general n_O will decrease as the

encounter radius increases; n_H may go either way.

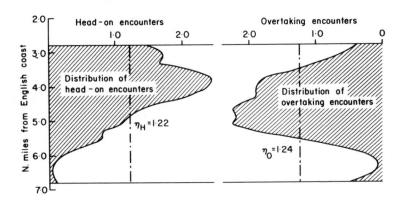

Fig. 17   Normalised distribution of $p_w(y)$ $p_e(y)$ and of
$(p_w^2(y)S_w^2 + p_e^2(y)S_e^2) / (S_w^2 + S_e^2)$ in Dover Strait from

Barratt and Hewson (1974). Clear weather

4.   COMPARISON OF POTENTIAL AND OBSERVED ENCOUNTERS

4.1   Head-on encounters: over-all numbers

A comparison of the calculated number of potential encoun
ters with the number actually observed indicates the accuracy
of the model, and should indicate whether mariners are taking
"early and decisive action" to avoid a close-quarter situatio
especially in fog, if the calculated number of encounters exceeds the number observed in practice.

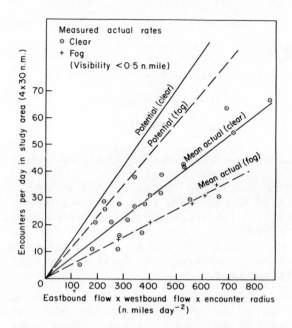

Fig. 18   Comparison of potential (calculated) and actual
(measured) head-on encounter rates in Dover Strait
study area 1972/3. Measured data from Barratt and
Hewson (1974)

The only available count of actual encounters is that
by Barratt and Hewson (1974). They observed time-lapse cine
films of radar echoes from traffic in the Dover Strait in an
area some 4 n.miles wide and 30 n.miles long straddling the
boundary between the English Inshore Zone and the Main Westbound
Lane. This area is shown in Fig. 15: it differs from that used
for the detailed traffic survey referred to in the previous
section. Ships in the area were considered to have an encounter
when their radar echoes merged, and the numbers of head-on encounters on each of 24 clear and 6 foggy days were noted and
plotted against the product of the eastbound and westbound flows
multiplied by the size of the echo, representing the encounter
radius   (Fig. 18).

We have calculated the number of head-on encounters as

$$N_H = 1.22 \times 0.18547 \times S_A \times S_B$$

where S_A and S_B are in ships per n.mile-hour. The measured
data in Fig. 18 refer to an area of 30 x 4 = 120 sq.n.miles
and the flow rates are given as ships/day through the area,
i.e., through gates 4 n.miles wide. Hence we would expect

$$N_H = 1.22 \times 0.18547 \times 120 \times 24 / (4 \times 24)^2 . S_A . S_B$$
$$= 0.071 \, S_A . S_B \text{ encounters/day}$$

where S_A and S_B are flow rates in ships/day through the area.

This line is plotted in Fig. 18 for an encounter radius
of 0.5 n.mile. As expected, it lies above, but only just abo
all the spots and the average ratio of actual to calculated
numbers of encounters is 54%. This means that just under hal
the ships, when faced with a head-on encounter within 0.5 n.m
in clear weather, take action to increase the miss distance t
more than this amount.

A similar calculation of the effect of the distribution
of traffic in fog can be carried out from the information in
Fig. 3 of Barratt and Hewson's report. This gives values of
n_H and n_O of 1.00 and 1.23, respectively. Thus the formula
for the number of potential head-on encounters in fog is 0.05
$S_A . S_B$ per day, fewer than in clear weather because very littl
of the eastbound traffic strayed into the Main Westbound Lane
This may be compared with the mean line drawn through Barratt
and Hewson's observations of slope 0.026. Thus it appears
that only 45% of potential head-on encounters within 0.5 n.mi
in fog become actual ones. This is discussed again in sectic
4.3.

4.2 *Head-on and overtaking encounters: distribution*

Barratt and Hewson showed the actual positions of a numk
of the encounters over the periods of time for which they gav
the traffic flow distributions. These were in the trapezoidal
study area shown in Fig. 15. For purposes of comparison, thi
area has been divided into six parallel strips, four of width
0.5 n.mile in the English Inshore Zone, and two of width 1.0
n.mile in the Main Westbound Lane. The numbers of encounters
observed in each strip during 92 hours of clear visibility
(better than 2 n.miles) and during 46 hours of fog (less than
0.5 n.mile), together with the numbers of potential encounter
calculated from the traffic distribution, are given in Table
II and plotted in Figs. 19 and 20. (The ordinates of Fig. 2C

are plotted at twice the scale of Fig. 19 to allow a direct comparison.)

Table II

Numbers of encounters in each strip								
		Clear: 92 hours				Fog: 46 hours		
Strip Position	Strip length	Head-on Calc. Meas.		Overtaking Calc Meas		Head-on Calc Meas		Overtaking Calc Meas
2.8-3.3	23.3	34.6	28	19.0	9	18.2	6	7.0	0
3.3-3.8	22.2	42.5	31	40.0	6	31.6	5	14.8	2
3.8-4.3	21.1	43.6	28	50.6	16	24.8	6	19.2	1
4.3-4.8	20.0	28.6	12	54.4	8	4.6	0	16.6	1
4.8-5.8	18.3	29.0	6	80.1	9	6.9	1	33.3	0
5.8-6.8	16.1	4.0	3	9.1	1	2.5	2	4.9	0
TOTAL		182.3	108 59%	253.2	49 19%	88.6	20 23%	95.8	4 4%

There appears to be reasonably good agreement between the potential and actual encounters as regards position, except that there are very few observed overtaking encounters in the Main Westbound Lane. The overtaking encounters are distributed more towards the centre of the study area than the head-on ones, whose peak occurs about 1 n.mile into the English Inshore Zone.

There is statistically highly significant evidence from Table II that mariners are more circumspect with respect to overtaking encounters than they are in head-on ones, and a higher proportion take avoiding action. This may be because the Collision Regulations are unambiguous and place the burden of avoidance manoeuvres on the faster ship.

4.3 The effect of reduced visibility

Table II also shows that fog makes mariners much more ready to avoid a close-quarter situation, and it reveals a more pronounced difference in this respect than does Fig. 18. The statistical sample of actual encounters is smaller, but the comparison with the calculations is more reliable because the measured traffic flows and distributions were used to calculate the relevant encounter rates. The decrease in the number of

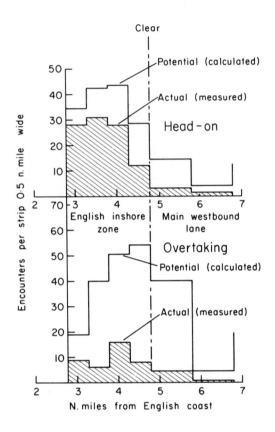

Fig. 19   Comparison of numbers of potential and actual encounters in study area south of Dover. Clear visibility;
sample 92 hours

actual encounters in fog from that calculated is greater than
that occurring in clear weather for both types of encounter
at the 0.1% level of significance. Barratt and Hewson had
shown a similar result, though with rather more experimental
scatter (Fig. 18).

5. CONCLUSIONS

    A mathematical model of marine traffic has been described
which allows the number of ship encounters to be calculated
from a knowledge of the traffic flow and its speed distributi
A number of graphs have been presented which show the variati

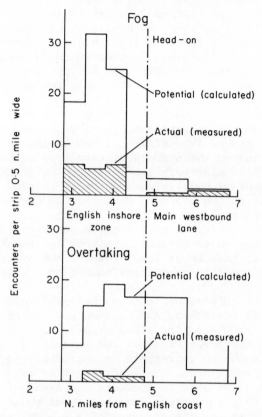

Fig. 20   Comparison of numbers of potential and actual encoun-
          ters in study area south of Dover.   Fog; sample length
          46 hours

in encounter rate with the angle and speed of crossing traffic
for a particular speed distribution of mainstream traffic.
These show that, when crossing a single uni-directional traffic
stream, an angle of between 45° and 60° will generally give
the fewest encounters, but that deviation by up to 20° from
the optimum will increase the number of encounters by less than
5%.   When crossing two uni-directional traffic streams without
change of course, a right angle crossing is best, but again,
deviation by up to 20° will give only a 5% increase in the
number of encounters.

These results are for a circular encounter area.   Results
are also given for an elliptical encounter area.   For an un-
skewed ellipse, the number of encounters with crossing traffic

is insensitive to crossing angle (within the range 40° to 110°
If the axis of the ellipse is at an angle to the direction of
mainstream traffic, then the number of encounters is more sensitive to crossing angle, being a minimum either at about 30°
(with the ellipse's major diameter in the direction of crossi
traffic) or at about 90° (with the ellipse's major diameter in
the direction of crossing traffic relative velocity).

The model is extended to cover head-on and overtaking encounters, and the variation of these with the proportion of
"rogues" is shown. The effect of the spread of ship speeds i
the mainstream on the numbers of each type of encounter is pr
sented: it has relatively little effect on head-on encounters
but the number of overtaking encounters is almost linearly
proportional to the standard deviation of ship speeds. For a
single vessel travelling with the mainstream, the number of
overtaking encounters during a given passage (in traffic simi
to that of the Dover Strait) is almost invariant with speed,
provided that this is at least that of the average ship. Slo
ships give rise to a very large number of overtaking encounte

The uneven distribution of mainstream traffic will affect
the number of overtaking and head-on encounters, and the effe
of this is calculated and shown graphically for a selected
area within the Dover Strait. The calculated distribution
pattern is shown to correspond approximately to that of actua
encounters in the area. This agreement is evidence that the
model is at least able to indicate the areas of sea most like
to contain ship encounters and this is of value in itself.
Further support for the accuracy of the model is provided by
the comparison of calculated and actual numbers of head-on
encounters for various flow rates, when it is seen that the
former always exceeds the latter, but sometimes by only a sma
amount.

The discrepancy in clear weather is typically between 40
and 50%, suggesting that just under half the mariners in the
Dover Strait are not prepared to accept a meeting situation
with a threatened miss distance of half a mile or less and
will take avoiding action. For overtaking situations, the
discrepancy is greater, as it is for both types of encounter
in foggy weather. It appears that only one mariner in 25 may
be prepared to overtake in fog with a clearance of half a mil
or less, and the rest will alter course to increase the separation distance. Curtis (p.175) has drawn attention to the
potential danger of overtaking too close; in fog, a distance
of at least 0.8 n.mile is advisable when overtaking a 12 -kn

ship, and even in clear weather a distance of at least 0.4 n.mile is needed in order to have time to avoid the slower vessel if it unexpectedly alters course.

REFERENCES

Barratt, M. J.   "Encounter rates in a marine traffic separation scheme", J. of Navigation, vol. 26, no. 4, Oct. 1973, pp. 458-65.

Barratt, M. J. and Hewson, C. M. T.   "Ship encounters and flow in selected areas of the Dover Strait", NPL report. Mar. Sci. R 117, Sept. 1974.

Cash, R. F. and Boribond, L. A.   "Traffic behaviour in the Dover Strait in poor and good visibility", NPL report Mar. Sci. R 110, July 1973.

Draper, J. and Bennett, C.   "Modelling encounter rates in marine traffic flows (with application to the Dover Strait)", Proceedings of Symposium on Marine Traffic Engineering, May 1972, pp. 16-32.   Royal Institute of Navigation and Royal Institution of Naval Architects, 1973.

Fujii, Y. and Shiobara, R.   "Studies in marine traffic engineering - the analysis of traffic accidents", J. of Navigation, vol. 24, no. 4, Oct. 1971, pp. 534.

Goodwin, E. M.   "A statistical study of ship domains",   PhD thesis, City of London Polytechnic, Jan. 1975.

Lewison, G. R. G.   "The risk of a ship encounter leading to a collision", National Maritime Institute report, R21, February 1978.

ENCOUNTERS, NEAR MISSES AND COLLISIONS AT SEA*

M.J. Barratt

(National Maritime Institute)

INTRODUCTION

One of the main aims of modelling marine traffic in open sea or coastal conditions is to predict the expected numbers of collisions when changes are made either in the traffic or the constraints under which it operates. Traffic changes might include total numbers and types of vessel, preferred routes and speeds. The constraints might include routeing schemes, collision avoidance regulations and topographical changes, for instance fixed structures in the sea.

Possibly the simplest way of predicting collision numbers is by way of the "encounter frequency", calculating the number of times that vessels may be expected to approach within some chosen distance of one another (e.g. Barratt (1976)), and obtaining a factor which relates this frequency to the known collision rate in some area for which good statistics are available. This procedure can be refined by subdividing the encounter into types (meeting, crossing, overtaking, etc.), and within certain limitations good predictions can be expected of the collision rates for traffic systems not too dissimilar from those for which the accident statistics are known.

The most obvious limitation is that, even in areas of relatively dense traffic, collisions are rare events, and therefore collision statistics can only be built up slowly over many years. By the time that sufficient numbers are available, the situation will probably have changed in important ways. For instance, in the Dover Strait region, collision statistics have been collected over a period of nearly 20 years (Brown and Wheatley (1972) and Bowdidge (1977)), but over that time in addition to traffic changes there has been the introduction of the Channel Navigation Information Service and at least one environmental change (the reduction in the amount of thick fog).

*©IMA; Controller HMSO London, 1979

Alternatively, in a new situation, there may exist very little useful history. For instance, there are now many fixed structures in the North Sea but there have as yet fortunately been few serious collisions. It is therefore difficult to estimate the likely collision frequency. If further we aspire to predict the likely effects of changes in the collision regulations, the information is even more sparse, because of the very few occasions on which the actions preceding an accident are known reliably. It therefore seems desirable to have a method of predicting collision rates based on events which occur more frequently than collisions, but are closely related to them, and this paper considers the concept of near misses in the maritime context.

SUBJECTIVE METHODS

First, it is worth noting that the near miss between aircraft - the "air miss" - is a well established concept, and is claimed to be closely related to collision potential (Baker and Morgan (1975)). A pilot is required to report when he considers his aircraft may have been endangered by the proximity of another aircraft to the extent that a definite risk of collision existed. The reporting scheme is on a voluntary basis for civil pilots and mandatory only for military pilots, but nevertheless sufficiently large numbers of "civil" incidents have been obtained for analytical purposes.

Such a scheme would be difficult to introduce in the maritime sphere. Apart from questions of custom and the ordinary practice of seamen, it is more difficult to define a near miss at sea, where vessels can approach quite close without causing surprise, than in the air, where any near approach almost by definition implies a breakdown of air traffic control.

As a check on the possible usefulness of such reports, the small number of complaints of collision risk that have reached the Department of Trade (mostly from the Dover Strait) over the last 3 years were studied (Table I).

Although not a good statistical sample, the impression is that their distribution by type does not correspond closely to that of collisions, as about one half of these "near misses" arose when vessels were on crossing courses, and involved cross-channel ferries, whereas the great majority of actual collisions have occurred between vessels on overtaking or near opposing courses (Brown and Wheatley (1972) and Bowdidge (1977) and ferries were rarely involved. The closest points of approach cannot be considered very reliable, but it is noticeal that much greater distances were considered dangerous in the crossing cases.

Table I

"Near misses" in the Dover Strait 1974-7

Type of encounter	Number	Closest point of approach
Overtaking	4	10m - 100m
Crossing	8	200m - 2km
Meeting	1	-
Multiple	2	400m

It appears, therefore, that complaints are not a reliable indicator of collision risk although this is not to say that well detailed reports of dangerous situations may not be useful for training (Nicholson (1976)). For analytical purposes, a model is proposed which will give an indication of collision risk based on firm data on encounter rates, but which is more directly related to the collision rate.

COLLISION AVOIDANCE MODEL

The model being developed is based on observations of traffic and collision avoidance, and uses the frequency of near misses in a temporal sense as an indication of collision frequency.

If we consider the tracks followed by vessels in a given area of sea over a period of time, we obtain a web of crossing paths, each crossing representing a point at which a collision could occur, if the relative timings of the vessels concerned were sufficiently unfortunate. As the size of the sample of tracks is built up, the number of crossings will rise quite rapidly to give a representative sample of possible conflict sites (Fig. 1), allowing a relatively quick estimate of the population of conflicts in the absence of avoidance action.

For each crossing the "time clearance" is defined as the difference in time between the centres of the two vessels reaching the crossing point. The sign convention is that the

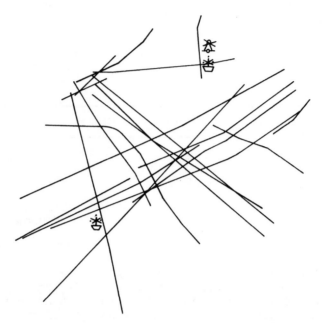

Fig. 1. Possible conflict sites
(1 Hour Period)

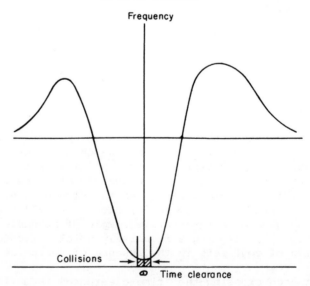

Fig. 2. Time clearance
frequency distribution

sign is positive if the line of sight between the two vessels rotates in an anticlockwise direction. A small range of time clearances about zero, which may be calculated (see Appendix), would actually correspond to collisions. A larger number would correspond to near misses, the subject of this paper.

In the absence of collision avoidance manoeuvres, it is assumed that vessels would be uniformly distributed in time (although some modification may be necessary to deal with regular scheduled services). It follows that all time clearances are equally likely, and the frequency distribution of time clearances should be uniform. Any deviation of the actual distribution should be due to collision avoidance action. If miss distances were used instead of time clearances, this useful property would not be obtained, since marine traffic is generally far from evenly distributed in space.

In Fig. 2, the frequency of occurrence of a given time clearance is shown for a hypothetical case which would be particular to the courses and speeds of the vessels concerned, the environment and other conditions. The effect of successful collision avoidance must be to decrease the frequency of time clearances close to zero, replacing them by larger time clearances to either side. (The expected effect of the collision regulations would be to increase mainly the positive time clearances.) The total area under the curve should be the same as that under the straight line representing an absence of collision avoidance action. The ratio of the frequency at the origin to the over-all frequency in the absence of manoeuvres is the ratio of actual to potential collisions.

The range of time clearances corresponding to collisions has been calculated for reasonably realistic ship shapes (see Appendix), and the result is shown in Fig. 3, where the collision interval is plotted against course difference for various pairs of vessels. It can be seen that for most cases the collision interval is less than 1 minute, so near misses might reasonably be defined as encounters with time clearances less than 1 or 2 minutes.

For time clearance frequency curves to be useful for predicting collision rates, their form must be well established near the origin, and this will require the analysis of a fairly large amount of data. It is hoped, however, that there will be sufficient similarity between their shapes for different types of encounter and environment to allow curves to be fitted to small amounts of data for the rarer types of situation.

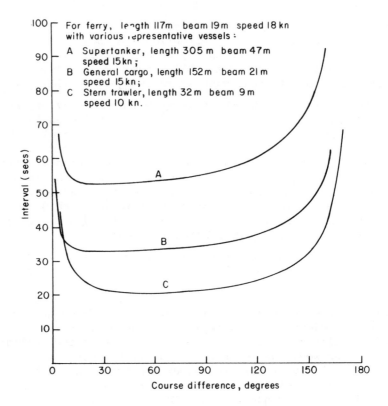

Fig. 3. Collision interval

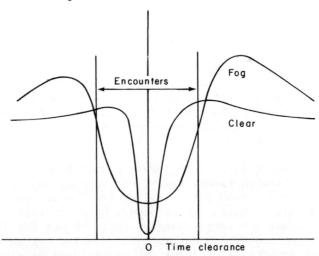

Fig. 4. Effect of reduced visibility - hypothetical forms
of time clearance frequency distributions

ENVIRONMENTAL EFFECTS

Great differences have been observed between clear visibility and foggy conditions both in the collision rates suffered
Brown and Wheatley (1972) and Bowdidge (1977)) and in the
collision avoidance maneouvres made (Barratt (1976)). The
apparent paradox is that collision rates have been much higher
in fog in spite of greater numbers of avoidance manoeuvres,
and of fewer encounters in which the vessels get within about
half a mile of each other. Clearly, any model aiming to predict
collisions from near misses must be capable of reflecting
these differences, and it is postulated that the effect of
reduced visibility may be to modify the shape of time clearance
distribution curves as shown in Fig. 4.

The curve for foggy conditions is comparatively flat-
bottomed, cutting the zero time clearance ordinate at a much
higher value than does the "clear visibility" curve. Thus the
collision rate is much higher, but the encounter rate, represented by the area under the curve where the frequency is reduced, is lower than for clear visibility. Such a result would
be consistent with the observed variability of collision avoidance manoeuvres in fog (Barratt (1976)), some of the extra
manoeuvres finally leading to closer encounters than were
originally threatened, and others to greater clearances than
were originally envisaged.

If the distribution curves for reduced visibility do ex-
hibit this characteristic , it will be possible to determine
their shape near the origin on the basis of less data than
would otherwise be needed. This is fortunate, as such data
are rare, but important, at least in North European waters.

SOME LIMITATIONS

Of course, not all very close approaches can be considered
near misses, and this is illustrated by the position over a
12 hour period for a limited area off Dover (Fig. 5). During
this time the vessels passing through had been identified visually, and the radar screen at Dover Strait Coastguard Station
had been photographed at 1 minute intervals.

All the positions of vessels within the chosen area over
the period were digitised (using a manually operated trace
reader), and the output converted to microfilm plots. Each
frame on the microfilm shows ten consecutive frames of film,
with the starting frame moved on by one each time. They can

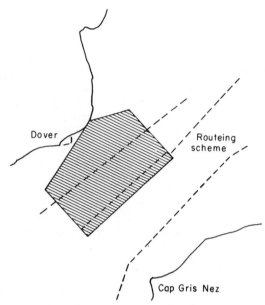

Fig. 5.   Area of analysis

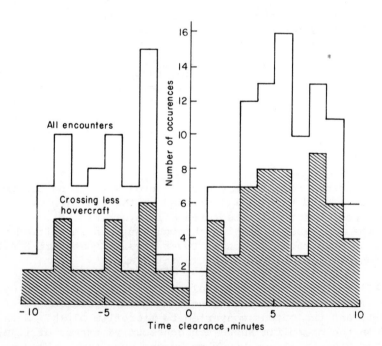

Fig. 6.   Distribution of time clearances - sample

thus be inspected to find the difference between the times at
which each pair of vessels pass the crossing point of their
tracks. As explained earlier this time difference provides an
attractive alternative to closest point of approach in the
analysis.

The result for this small sample is shown in Fig. 6 which
shows the numbers of occasions when each time difference
(rounded to the nearest minute) occurred. Naturally there are
not enough occurrences to define the curve shapes well, but the
general features expected are present; the reduction in encounter
numbers near the origin, the increase on either side, and the
tendency towards "positive" rather than "negative" time
differences.

If we focus attention on crossing encounters, because
these were the largest class, and leave out hovercraft, because their speed and stopping ability were so very different
from the other vessels, we are left with only one occasion on
which the time difference was less than 1 minute, and this was
actually a "negative" crossing encounter, with the give way
vessel apparently standing on. However, on examination this
promising "near miss" turned out to be a safe manoeuvre, the
crossing vessel making a course change to cross the traffic
lane at right angles just after one of the through vessels
had passed (Fig. 7).

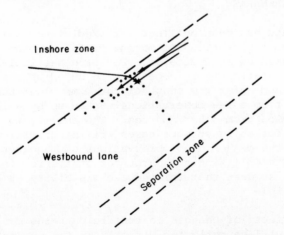

Fig. 7. Closest observed encounter

This case illustrates the difficulties of this approach
and shows the need to link any mathematical modelling with a
fairly close study of what actually happens. In this particular case the crossing vessel was trying to maximise his distance, not from the vessel behind which he passed, but from
those following. The situation was also constrained by the
need to make a course change to comply with the collision
regulations. This example also suggests that a refinement in
the definition of time clearance, to take account of its expected value shortly before the tracks cross, may be appropria

DATA GATHERING

The major aim of the proposed prediction method is to
make the best possible use of any traffic and encounter data
available, and work has been started to obtain such data from
photographic records.

The overall traffic patterns will of course be particular to the region, but the interactions between vessels, as
expressed by their time clearances or other chosen parameters,
should have more general applications. In transferring such
data to other regions, account must be taken not only of the
different types of encounter, as expressed by relative courses
and speeds of the vessels concerned, but also the local restrictions to navigation, traffic densities and environment.

CONCLUDING REMARKS

A method has been outlined for predicting collision rates
from limited observations of marine traffic, using the numbers
of near misses as an indicator. For each particular area
under consideration it is necessary to build up a sample of
conflicts, and infer the shape of the time clearance distribution curve from a few observations backed up by a larger body
of information from other sources. The ability to define
this curve for at least some cases will be crucial to the
success of the method, and observations of manoeuvres in fog,
combined with collision and encounter statistics for these
conditions, suggest that for reduced visibility at least this
may be possible.

The effects of changes in traffic patterns can be found,
since they will be reflected directly in the numbers and types
of conflicts, and the probable effects of changes in the collision regulations could be inferred by altering the distribution
of types of response.

It is recognised that there can be no prediction as reliable as a good sample of collisions, but this is what we are trying to avoid. The aim is to eliminate the effect, even if this means that it can never be adequately studied.

REFERENCES

Baker, C.B. and Morgan, S.L. (1975) "Analysis of the civil airmiss situation in the United Kingdom, and its relation to collision risk", Civil Aviation Authority. DORA Report 7403.

Barratt, M.J. (1976) "Collision avoidance manoeuvres in restricted visibility", Journal of Navigation 29.4.

Bowdidge, I.D. (1977) "Collisions and strandings in the Dover Strait area 1960-76", National Maritime Institute R12

Brown, I.S.H. and Wheatley, J.H.W.W. (1972) "Circumstances of Collisions and Strandings in the Dover Strait area 1958-71", NPL Report Mar. Sci. R101.

Marks, B.L. (1963) "Air Traffic Control Separation Standards and Collision Risk", RAE Tech. Note Math. 91.

Nicolson, D. (1976) "Reporting near misses at sea", Journal of Navigation 29.4 (Forum).

Webster, W.C. (1974) "When is collision unavoidable?", 10th Symposium on Naval Hydrodynamics, Cambridge, Mass.

APPENDIX

COLLISION INTERVAL

A collision is possible when the tracks of two vessels cross. It will occur if they reach the crossing point at the same time, or if the elapsed time between their reaching that point is within limits dependent upon their sizes, speeds and crossing angle. The following analysis calculates the range of elapsed times over which a collision will take place, here referred to as the collision interval.

Consider first two vessels of negligible beam, with lengths ℓ_A, ℓ_B, speeds V_A, V_B.

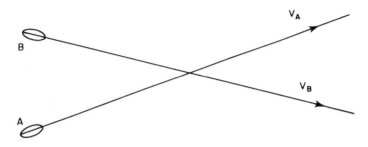

Let the bow of vessel A reach the crossing point at time O, then the stern of vessel A will pass the crossing point at time ℓ_A/V_A. Vessel B will strike vessel A if its bow

reaches the crossing point between times O and ℓ_A/V_A; i.e., if the elapsed time between A reaching the crossing and B reaching the crossing is between O and ℓ_A/V_A.

For A to strike B, B must be passing the crossing point at time O; that is, its bow must pass the crossing point between times $-\ell_B/V_B$ and O. This means that the elapsed time between A reaching the crossing and B reaching the crossing must be between $-\ell_B/V_B$ and O.

So the collision interval, which is equal to the range of elapsed time $= \ell_A/V_A - (- \ell_B/V_B) = \ell_A/V_A + \ell_B/V_B$.
For a vessel of finite beam, the position is more complex. For convenience, the ship hull shapes can be approximated by straight sided bodies with semi-circular ends of radii r_A, r_B

(Webster (1974)). As before, the collision interval is the range of elapsed time between A reaching the crossing and B reaching the crossing which gives a collision, that is the difference of the times at which the bow of B can just touch the stern of A and vice versa. The ship positions at these times are shown in Fig. 8. The condition for a collision just to occur is a "kissing" contact between the semi-circular portions so that the normal components of velocity of the two ships at their point of contact are equal.

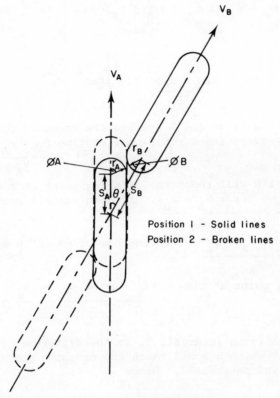

Fig. 8. Collision geometry

This gives

$$V_A \cos \phi_A = V_B \cos \phi_B,$$

with

$$\theta = \phi_A - \phi_B$$

and

$$\frac{s_A}{\sin\phi_B} = \frac{s_B}{\sin\phi_A} = \frac{r_A + r_B}{\sin\theta}.$$

Now since

$$v_A \cos (\theta + \phi_B) = V_B \cos \phi_B,$$

we have

$$\frac{v_B}{v_A} = \cos\theta - \sin\theta \tan\phi_B$$

giving

$$\tan \phi_B = \frac{\cos\theta - v_B/v_A}{\sin\theta}.$$

Also $S_A = (r_A + r_B)\dfrac{\sin\phi_B}{\sin\theta} = \dfrac{(r_A + r_B)}{\sin\theta} \sin\left\{\tan^{-1}\left[\dfrac{\dfrac{V_B}{\cos\theta - V_A}}{\sin\theta}\right]\right\}$

and similarly $S_B = \dfrac{(r_A + r_B)}{\sin\theta} \sin\left\{\tan^{-1}\left[\dfrac{\dfrac{V_A}{V_B} - \cos\theta}{\sin\theta}\right]\right\}$.

If the bow of vessel A reaches the crossing point at time 0 and both vessels reach position 1 at time $\dfrac{S_A + r_A}{V_A}$, then the bow of vessel B will reach the crossing point at time $t_1 = \dfrac{S_A + r_A}{V_A} - \dfrac{(\ell_2 + S_B - r_B)}{V_B}$. If both vessels reach position 2 at time $\dfrac{\ell_A - S_A - r_A}{V_A}$, then the bow of vessel B will reach the crossing point at time $t_2 = \dfrac{\ell_A - S_A - r_A}{V_A} + \dfrac{S_B - r_B}{V_B}$.

The collision interval, T, is the difference between the times at which B would reach the crossing point when in position 1 and position 2. Hence

$$T = t_2 - t_1 = \left| \dfrac{\ell_A - 2r_A - 2S_A}{V_A} + \dfrac{\ell_B - 2r_B + 2S_B}{V_B} \right| .$$

Putting $2r_A = b_A$, $2r_B = b_B$, we have

$$T = \left| \dfrac{1}{V_A}\left[\ell_A + b_A - \dfrac{(b_A + b_B)}{\sin\theta} \sin\left\{\tan^{-1}\left[\dfrac{\dfrac{V_B}{V_A} - \cos\theta}{\sin\theta}\right]\right\}\right] \right.$$

$$\left. + \dfrac{1}{V_B}\left[\ell_B - b_B + \dfrac{(b_A + b_B)}{\sin\theta} \sin\left\{\tan^{-1}\left[\dfrac{\dfrac{V_A}{V_B} - \cos\theta}{\sin\theta}\right]\right\}\right] \right| .$$

The collision interval thus calculated approaches that for a thin ship for most crossing cases but deviates greatly for near head on and overtaking cases (Fig. 3).

AN ANALYSIS OF THE DANGERS OF SHIPS OVERTAKING *

R.G. Curtis

(National Maritime Institute)

1. INTRODUCTION

In most parts of the ocean ships are free to move about
in any direction and so ships meet at a variety of different
angles. However, the situation is different in the Dover
Strait and other similar regions where the high density of
through traffic has made it necessary to introduce traffic
routeing schemes, under which ships are recommended to move
unidirectionally along one of two or more shipping lanes. In
the Dover Strait there are two main lanes, for use by eastbound
and westbound ships. Traffic routeing reduces the total number
of encounters, but increases the number of overtaking encounters.
The proportion of overtaking encounters in the main lanes is
therefore greatly increased. For example (see Lewison, Fig. 11,
p.146 in this volume) routeing in the Dover Strait (with 1%
of through rogues) has increased the proportion of potential
overtaking encounters from 27 to 95%.

The master of a ship is often uncertain of the future
manoeuvres other ships intend to carry out; he is also aware
that because of the slow response of his own ship it may take
a considerable time to effect an avoidance manoeuvre. Because
of this uncertainty mariners try to keep an area around their
ships free from other vessels; this area is often known as a
"domain". These ship domains have been studied by Fujii and
Tanaka (1971) and Goodwin (1975), who have used radar and
other methods to observe the way in which ships are manoeuvred.
The domain of a ship can be regarded as the region around
that ship which the master is able to keep clear of other
ships, because he fears that he may be unable to avoid collision if a ship in this region makes a sudden course alteration.

This paper describes a theoretical model of an overtaking
encounter, and calculates the minimum safe overtaking distance
*© IMA; Controller HMSO London, 1979

175

for ships. This is defined as the least track separation
during overtaking at which the overtaking ship could avoid
collision if the overtaken ship altered course through a right
angle when the two ships were in the most disadvantageous
relative positions. On comparing the theoretical minimum
safe overtaking distance with the observed behaviour of ships
and with the ship domains measured by Goodwin and Fujii, it
is shown that many ships are running a small but finite risk
of collision when they overtake.

2. THE MODEL

2.1 General description

The model describes a situation in which a ship (A), with
speed v_A, is being overtaken by a faster ship (B), of speed
v_B. They are on parallel tracks a distance D apart (Fig. 1).
Initially when A and B are at A_0 and B_0, B is still a distance
H astern of A and bears an angle of θ abaft A's beam. At this
time A starts to deviate from its track and turns sharply
towards B's track. If B does not have time to make a collision
avoidance manoeuvre, then under certain conditions a collision
will result. This depends on the track separation and exactly
when A makes its turn and the dimensions of the two ships.

The course change by A is often anticipated by ship B.
In this case ship B will commence its avoidance manoeuvre at
about the same time as ship A and there should be no danger.
A collision may occur when the turn by A is sudden and
unexpected. This is the situation that will be analysed. An
unexpected turn is most likely to occur in fog; the cause
may be a rogue or a crossing vessel appearing out of the fog
or a patch of radar clutter, or a small yacht which was not
observed until almost under the ship's bows.

In this analysis it is assumed that A's turn is through
a right angle, and that for practical purposes A's track is
an arc of a circle of radius R. The ships are assumed to be
narrow and of finite lengths ℓ_A and ℓ_B; consequently there is
then a zone of potential danger (shaded in Fig. 1) such that
if A starts to turn when B is within this zone, a collision
will result unless B takes avoiding action in time. The leading edge of the danger zone corresponds to B's stern just being
caught by A's bow, and the trailing edge corresponds to B's
bow just striking A's stern. For a position within the zone,

the "collision time" is defined as that time elapsing between
the instant at which A's track first deviates from a straight
line and the time when A just reaches B's track. Because of
the finite size of the ships, a collision may take place before
the centre of A reaches B's track. This is considered in more
detail below. The collision time is a function of the geometry
of the encounter.

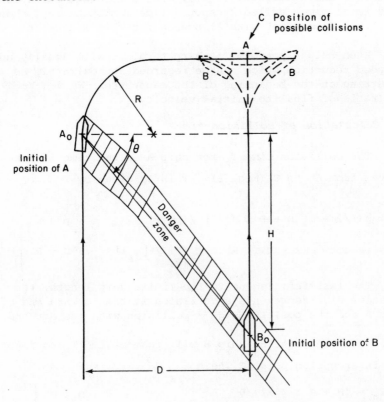

Fig. 1 The overtaking situation

     If A should turn through an angle other than a right
angle, there is also a risk of collision, and the danger zone
will be the same width in the direction of motion of ship B
as that shown in Fig. 1. If the turn is less than a right
angle the danger zone moves ahead and if it is more than a
right angle it moves astern. The collision time is not
significantly affected by small variations from a right angle
turn.

The time required for B to take avoidance action is made up of the mariner's reaction time and his ship's time to manoeuvre clear. The former has been studied by means of experiments on a radar ship simulator (Curtis (1978)) and the results are given here; the latter is known from ship handling characteristics (Gill (1976), Lewison (1973) and Clarke, Patterson and Wooderson (1973)). For B to avoid collision, this total time, called "response time", must be less than the "collision time" with allowance for ship dimensions.

When ship A performs a sharp turn, it will usually under a speed reduction which can be regarded approximately as occurring at the beginning of the manoeuvre. We denote by r the ratio of final to initial velocity.

2.2 Calculation of collision time

The collision time T_A for ship A is the time it takes to travel from A_0 to C (Fig. 1). This is given by:

$$
\left.
\begin{aligned}
T_A &= [\,(\pi/2 - 1)\,R + D \pm \ell_A/2\,] \,/\, [\,v_A r\,] \qquad : D \geqslant R \\
    &= \{R\,\cos^{-1}[(R - D)\,/\,R] \pm \ell_A/2\} \,/\, [\,v_A r\,] \quad : D < R.
\end{aligned}
\right\} \qquad (1)
$$

The last term is due to the finite ship length; the negative sign represents a collision at the forward end of ship A and the positive sign a collision with its aft end.

From the point B_0 ship B will take a time T_B to reach the interception point C where

$$
\left.
\begin{aligned}
T_B &= (H + R \pm \ell_B/2)/v_B \qquad\qquad\qquad : D \geqslant R \\
    &= [\,H + (2RD - D^2)^{1/2} \pm \ell_B/2\,] \,/\, v_B \quad : D < R.
\end{aligned}
\right\} \qquad (2)
$$

2.3 Calculation of relative position

If the two ships are to collide at C then $T_A = T_B$ and hence equations (1) and (2) give

$$
\left.\begin{aligned}
&= [v_B/(v_A r)] \ [\ (\pi/2 - 1) \ R + D] \ - R \pm [\ \ell_B/2 + \ell_A v_B/(2 v_A r)] \\
&\qquad\qquad\qquad\qquad\qquad\qquad\qquad\qquad\qquad\qquad : D \geqslant R \\
&= [\ (v_B/(v_A r)] \ R \ \cos^{-1} [\ (R-D)/R] \ - (2RD-D^2)^{1/2} \pm \\
&\quad [\ \ell_B/2 + \ell_A v_B/(2 v_A r)] \ : D < R \ .
\end{aligned}\right\} \quad (3)
$$

f collision is to occur, ship A must start to turn at A_0 when
is given by

$$
\theta = \tan^{-1} (H/D) \ . \qquad\qquad (4)
$$

his gives the relative position in which a right angle turn
vould result in collision.

If the two ships are travelling at the same speed then
$_A = v_B$, and equations (3) and (4) reduce to

$$
\theta_v = \tan^{-1} \{[\ (\pi/2 - 1 - r) \ R + D]/(rD)\} \ : D \geqslant R. \quad (4A)
$$

his gives θ_v the relative position of maximum danger for ships
:ravelling at the same speed and keeping station.

.4   Calculation of the minimum safe overtaking distance

Let T be the response time of ship B, then rearranging
:quation (1) gives the minimum safe overtaking distance D as

$$
\left.\begin{aligned}
D &= T \ v_A r - [\ (\pi/2) - 1] \ R \pm \ell_A/2 \qquad : D \geqslant R \\
&= R \{1 - \cos [\ (T \ v_A r \pm \ell_A/2)/R] \} \quad : D < R.
\end{aligned}\right\} \quad (5)
$$

D is a monotonically increasing function of T and v_A. Hence
this equation can be used to determine a single valued minimum
safe overtaking distance as a function of v_A for a given value
of T and r.

.5   Risk of collision

When the tracks of two ships A and B cross, as they do at
C (Fig. 1), each is exposed to being struck by the other for
a finite length of time. The total time during which either
ship is at risk can be called the "collision risk time" and is

a function of the ship lengths and speeds. It is invariant
under changes of encounter angle, provided the crossing angle
is not small so that the ship widths and hydrodynamic interact
effects are negligibly small. If the two ship courses are
such that they are going to collide, then the collision risk
time multiplied by the speed of ship B defines a range of
positions for ship B which will result in collision. This
range gives the width, in the direction of motion, of the dan
zone marked in Fig. 1. Ship B will be exposed to risk while
it is in this danger zone. The time it takes to pass through
the zone, which is moving forward with ship A, is known as the
"risk exposure time" and is derived by dividing the danger
zone width by the relative velocity of the two ships.

From equation (2) ship A will be in danger of hitting B
for a time ℓ_B/v_B and from equation (1) ship B will be able to
hit A for a time $\ell_A/(v_A r)$. So the "collision risk time" is

$$\ell_A/(v_A r) + \ell_B/v_B.$$

During this time the overtaking ship B will travel a distance

$$\varepsilon = v_B \, \ell_A \, / \, (v_A r) + \ell_B. \tag{6}$$

Therefore for a collision to occur ship B must be within
$\varepsilon/2$ of B_0 at the start of the turn. Since both ships are
moving in the same direction the overtaking rate is $(v_B - v_A)$
and so "risk exposure time", or time during which a turn by
ship A could result in a collision, is

$$T_e = [\, v_B \ell_A \, / \, (v_A r) + \ell_B] \, / \, (v_B - v_A). \tag{7}$$

If T_p is the mean time interval between ships overtaking at
less than the minimum safe overtaking distance on one side of
the ship, then the probability that a turn by the overtaken
ship will result in a collision is

$$P = T_e/T_p : T_e \ll T_p. \tag{8}$$

2.6 Sensitivity to angle and radius of turn

If the model is to predict accurately the behaviour of
the physical system it is designed to describe, the results
should be relatively insensitive to small variations in those
parameters which cannot be measured or predicted accurately.
The angle through which the ship turns is one such parameter.
Suppose the ship does not turn exactly through a right angle
as assumed; let the angle be

$$\pi/2 + \delta\phi \text{ where } |\delta\phi| \ll 1.$$

Then equation (1) becomes

$$T_A = [(\pi/2 - 1) R + D \pm \ell_A/2] / [v_A r] + O (\delta\phi^2) :$$

$$D \geqslant R (1 + \delta\phi). \tag{9}$$

Thus the variation in the collision time is of the order $\delta\phi^2$.

Equation (2) becomes

$$T_B = (H + R \pm \ell_B/2) / v_B + O (\delta\phi) : D \geqslant R (1 + \delta\phi) \tag{10}$$

and equations (3) and (4) become

$$H = [v_B/(v_A r)] [\pi/2 - 1) R + D] - R$$

$$\pm [\ell_B/2 + \ell_A v_B/(2v_A r)] + O(\delta\phi) : D \geqslant R (1 + \delta\phi) \tag{11}$$

$$\theta = \tan^{-1} (H/D) + O (\delta\phi) : D \geqslant R (1 + \delta\phi). \tag{12}$$

Equation (12) shows that the initial relative position
of the ships which result in a collision varies as order $\delta\phi$.
Consequently the model cannot predict the relative position
of maximum danger.

Equation (5) becomes, by transposing equation (9),

$$D = T v_A r - [(\pi/2) - 1] R \pm \ell_A/2 + O (\delta\phi^2) : D \geqslant R (1 + \delta\phi). \tag{13}$$

This gives the minimum safe overtaking distance and thus is
correct to order $\delta\phi^2$. Consequently small variations from a
right angle turn do not significantly affect the minimum safe
overtaking distance. For example if the turn differs from a
right angle by 10° (0.17 rad) the error term is of order
G

0.17^2 or 3%.

It turns out also that errors in the prediction of the radius of turn are not very significant. For example an error of 20% in the radius of turn will typically produce a 3% error in the minimum safe overtaking distance.

Equations (7) and (8), which predict the risk exposure time and the probability of a turn resulting in a collision, are derived without resorting to the right angle turn assumption or using the radius of turn. Consequently the risk exposure time is invariant under small changes in the angle and radius of turn of ship A.

Thus we can say that the model is robust, with the single exception of the prediction of the angle θ, the relative position of maximum danger.

3. AN OVERTAKING EXAMPLE

3.1 Observed track separations

In order to see how mariners are handling overtaking situations in the Dover Strait, photographic records of a radar covering the main westbound lane in the vicinity of Dover have been studied. The study covered the overtaking of ships with speeds between 12 and 13 knots. A histogram giving the number of overtakings during a 7 day period as a function of track separation is presented in Fig. 2. During this period 2860 n miles were steamed by ships whose speeds were between 12 and 13 knots. These results indicate that a 12 knot ship will be overtaken on each side by another ship whose track separation is less than 0.9 n mile once in about every 11 hours of its passage time.

3.2 Behaviour of a VLCC

The handling characteristics of VLCCs have been studied by Gill (1976), Lewison (1973) and Clarke, Patterson and Wooderson (1973). A turning manoeuvre by a 325 metre VLCC is illustrated in Fig. 3, which was obtained from a computer simulation carried out at the NMI. Initially when the ship's centre was at the origin its rudder was moved to hard-a-starboard and the engine telegraph put to full ahead. Almost immediately the ship started to swing, but it took 1½ or 2 minutes before the ship started to deviate appreciably from

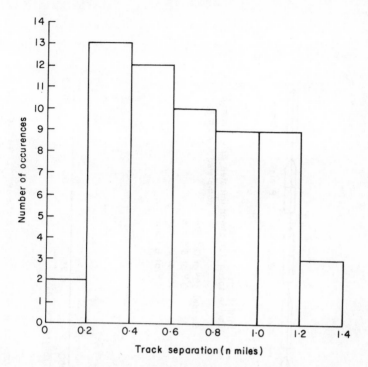

Fig. 2   Histogram of observed overtaking track separations

its straight course. When it did so its trajectory was
approximately an arc of a circle of radius 0.4 n mile. After
3 minutes the rudder was put amidships and then opposite
rudder was used to prevent the swing after the ship had turned
through a right angle. During this manoeuvre the ship maintained almost constant speed; the speed loss due to the turn
was matched by the increase in engine speed. Fig. 3 shows
that this ship would require about 4 minutes from the operation
of the rudder to achieve 0.5 km transfer, which would be
required to manoeuvre clear of a ship of its own size.

It should be noted that time in the overtaking model is
measured from the instant at which the ship starts to deviate
from its track as seen on radar and is consequently 1½ or 2
minutes different from the time measured in Fig. 3 from the
instant at which the helm was moved.

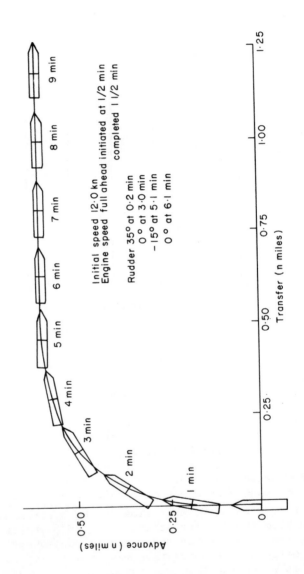

Fig. 3   Turning manoeuvre of a VLCC in 36 metres of water

3.3 Mariner's reactions times

A series of experiments using a radar ship simulator to determine mariners' reaction times in fog has been conducted (Curtis (1978)). The subjects for the tests were (i) mariners holding master's or mate's foreign going certificates, and (ii) pilots. They were asked to go into a booth equipped with a relative motion north up stabilised radar display, a plotting table, auto pilot, steering controls and engine controls. They were told that they, as master, had been called to the bridge of their ship because of reduced visibility. An overtaking situation similar to that analysed in this paper was simulated, and after 18 minutes on the bridge the overtaken ship was made to turn through a right angle. The reaction times were measured from the instant the overtaken ship A started to deviate from its straight course to the instant a helm or engine order was given by the subject. The reaction times of the two types of subject were similar (Fig. 4); the mean was 2.93 minutes with a standard deviation of 0.71 minute. This reaction time of about 3 minutes in fog should be less in good visibility since the mariners would have noticed a VLCC starting to swing a minute or two before its course alteration was observed on the radar. Thus in good visibility the mariner's reaction time might well be as small as $1\frac{1}{2}$ minutes.

3.4 An example to be studied

As an example of the ship to be overtaken consider the 200000 tonne tanker steaming at 12.0 knots described in section 3.2. The most dangerous overtaking ship is likely to be a similar VLCC. This will have a response time of about 7 minutes in fog, composed of 3 minutes mariner's reaction time and 4 minutes required by the ship to manoeuvre clear. However, in good visibility the response time would probably be reduced to $5\frac{1}{2}$ minutes.

Results of survey (NPL (March and July 1971); Cash and Marcus (1972)) show that the typical overtaking ship is a 10000 GRT cargo vessel of 150 m length and proceeding at 15.5 knots. This ship is more manoeuvreable than a VLCC and has a response time of 5 minutes in fog; 3 minutes mariner's reaction time in fog and 2 minutes to manoeuvre clear (Chislett and Strom-Tejsen (1965)). The results of section 3.1 show that it overtakes a 12 knots ship about every 11 hours per side at less than 0.9 n mile track separation.

The overtaking VLCC serves in the next section as an example to illustrate lane width requirements in traffic separation schemes, whereas the typical overtaking cargo ships facilitates the calculation of general risk.

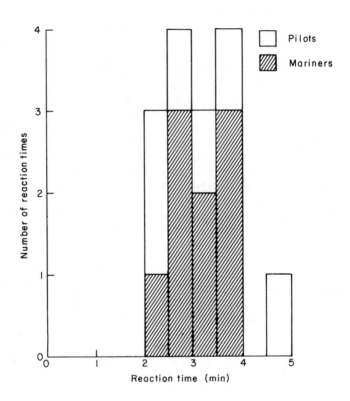

Fig. 4   Histogram of reaction times to a sudden turn by a
         vessel measured on a radar simulator

4. RESULTS

4.1 Collision time

Fig. 5 illustrates the way in which the collision time
varies with track separation for different speeds of the
overtaken ship. Once the track separation is greater than
the radius of turn, the relationship between collision time
and track separation becomes linear.

It can also be seen that it is dangerous for a VLCC with
a response time in fog of 7 minutes (section 3.4) to overtake
a 12.0 knots ship at less than 1.3 n miles. Good visibility
would reduce the response time to about 5½ minutes, in which
case it would not be safe to overtake at less than 1.0 n mile.
For this situation the track separation should be increased

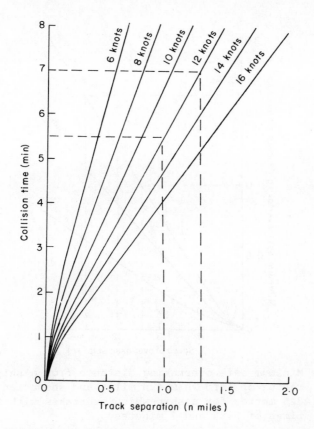

Fig. 5   Collision time for overtaken ship A of length 325 metres
         and radius of turn 0.4 n mile

by 0.3 n mile in fog. These results also highlight the neces-
sity for alertness on the part of the ships' crews so as to
reduce the response time as much as possible when overtaking
other ships.

4.2 Minimum safe overtaking distance

Fig. 6 shows the minimum safe overtaking distance against
speed of overtaken ship for overtaking ships with response
times of 3, 5 and 7 minutes. Both Figs. 5 and 6 show that a
greater track separation should be allowed when overtaking a
fast ship than a slow one. For instance in fog with a response
time of 7 minutes a ship whose speed is 12.0 knots has a minimum safe overtaking distance of 1.3 n miles; if the ship being

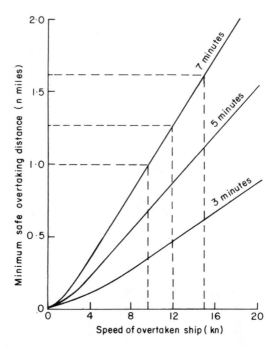

Fig. 6   Minimum safe overtaking distance from a ship whose
         radius of turn is 0.4 n mile and whose length is
         325 metres for a ship which overtakes with response
         times of 3, 5 and 7 minutes

overtaken increases its speed by. say, 3.0 knots to 15.0 knots
then the minimum safe overtaking distance increases by 0.3 n
mile to 1.6 n miles.

    Fig. 6 shows how the model can be used to determine speed
limits for lanes of limited width. If a traffic separation
scheme is limited in width to 2.0 n miles then a ship travelling in the centre of the main lane would force any overtaking
vessel to do so at a separation of less than 1.0 n mile. Fig.
6 shows that for ships with response times of 7 minutes, for
example a VLCC in fog, it would be unsafe to overtake this
vessel if its speed exceeded 9.7 knots. This will in effect
therefore determine a safe upper limit of speed in these
conditions.

4.3 Overtaking risk

Equations 7 and 8 can be used to determine the risk a ship runs every time it makes a sudden unexpected turn. Consider a VLCC in fog proceeding along the Dover Strait at 12.0 knots. Inserting details of the typical overtaking ship from section 3.4 into equation (7) gives the risk exposure time T_e to be 5.4 minutes. The observations described in section 3.1 show that the ship is overtaken about every 11 hours of passage per side at a distance less than the minimum safe overtaking distance of 0.9 n mile. Thus T_p is 11 hours and equation (8) gives a probability of 0.8% that a sudden right angle turn will result in a collision if, before making his turn, the overtaken ship does not make sure that no other ship is overtaking him dangerously close.

5. CONCLUDING REMARKS

A model of an overtaking encounter has been constructed and graphs of minimum safe overtaking distance presented. These graphs, with observations of the current rate of close overtaking, show that a large tanker proceeding in fog in the Dover Strait runs a 0.8% chance of collision each time it makes a sudden unexpected turn: i.e., if it turns without first ensuring that any overtaking ship, within the minimum safe overtaking distance, is aware of its intention to make the turn.

The results presented are relevant to the design of traffic separation schemes. They help the planner decide the required lane widths. If these are restricted by geographic considerations the model suggests the maximum speed of ship which can be overtaken with safety in different conditions.

It is interesting to compare the results of this analysis with the results measured by Fujii and Tanaka(1971) and Goodwin(1975) and with observations of ship tracks recorded on radar. These authors have not specifically studied the situation in the Dover Strait but their observations of ship domains suggest that mariners in this area have a ship domain of about 0.22 n mile (Fujii) and 0.8 n mile (Goodwin). This considerable difference may be because Fujii's results were obtained by linear extrapolation from observations of small ships. Goodwin's observed ship domain is in agreement with predictions of minimum safe overtaking distance (or theoretical ship domain as it may be called).

Both Goodwin's results and observations (Fig. 3) show
that some ships are passing with a track separation less than
the minimum safe overtaking distance calculated from this
model; and indeed observations of radar films (section 3.1)
show that a ship proceeding at 12.0 knots is overtaken on each
side at a distance less than the minimum safe overtaking distance on average once in about every 11 hours of its passage
time. This means that many ships, when they overtake another
vessel, are taking a risk of which they are probably unaware.
It is hoped that the results in this paper will be of practical
help to the mariner in reducing his chance of being involved
in an overtaking collision.

6. FURTHER APPLICATIONS OF THE MODEL

The analysis applies equally well to the head on as to
the overtaking situation. The results of collision time and
track separation given in Fig. 5 remain unaltered by the
change in direction of ship B; similarly the minimum safe
overtaking distance and ship speed results presented in Fig
6 still apply if one regards the minimum safe overtaking distance as the minimum safe head on track separation. The most
noticeable difference is that the risk exposure time is reduced
since the dangerous situation is resolved much more rapidly
by the greater relative velocity in the head on encounter.
Equation 7 which gives the risk exposure time acquires a positive sign in the denominator for the head on case. The model
can thus be of further use in the design of routeing schemes,
because Fig. 6 shows separation zone requirements between main
lanes.

The concept of a minimum safe overtaking distance or a
minimum safe head on track separation can be extended to any
angle of approach. In general it can be regarded as a theoretical ship domain, that is an area around the "own" ship
which should be kept clear of other ships, because the master
of own ship may not be able to avoid collision if the other
ship makes a sudden and unexpected manoeuvre. It is planned
to develop this theoretical ship domain and by comparison with
the ship domain measured by Goodwin (1975) to deduce a risk
factor for a traffic flow pattern.

REFERENCES

Cash, R.F. and Marcus, N.G., "Ship identification in the Dover Strait using helicopters 1 - 4 May 1972", NPL, Mar. Sci. Report R104 (December 1972).

Chislett, M.S. and Strom-Tejsen, J., "Planar motion mechanism tests and full-scale steering and manoeuvring predictions for a "Mariner" class vessel", Hydro and Aerodynamics Laboratory, Lyngby, Denmark, report, Hy-6, April 1965.

Clarke, D., Patterson, D.R. and Wooderson, R.K., "Manoeuvring trials with the 193,000 tonne deadweight tanker "Esso Bernicia"", J. R. Inst. N. Arch., April 1973, 89.

Curtis, R.G., "Determination of mariners' reaction times", J. Navigation, 1978, 38, 408.

Fujii, Y. and Tanaka, K., "Traffic capacity", J. Navigation, 1971, 24, 543.

Gill, A.D., "The identification of manoeuvring equations from ship trial results", NMI R3 (August 1976).

Goodwin, E.M., "A statistical study of ship domains", J. Navigation, 1975, 28, 328.

Lewison, G.R.G., "The development of ship manoeuvring equations", NPL Report, Ship 176 (December 1973).

"Marine Traffic in the Dover Strait - An exploratory survey and analysis of collisions" NPL, Eng. Sci. Report 1 - 71, (March 1971).

"Marine Traffic in the Dover Strait - A survey of traffic: 27th April 1971 to 29th April 1971", NPL Mar. Sci. Report 2 - 71 (July 1971).

MATHEMATICAL MODELLING OF SHIP MANOEUVRING*

A. D. Gill

(National Maritime Institute)

1. INTRODUCTION

The representation of ship manoeuvring behaviour using mathematical models is now a well established technique. The development of ship handling simulators for the training of mariners and for research into ship controllability has provided the main impetus for the development of complex mathematical models able to describe ship manoeuvring performance over a wide range of conditions. The general model described here has been developed at the National Maritime Institute primarily for use in ship handling simulators. A simpler special model is also described; this contains the restriction of constant or slowly varying engine speed. This simpler model may often be quite adequate for less demanding applications such as the prediction of ship manoeuvring performance at constant engine speed, ship controllability studies and auto-pilot design.

The determination of a mathematical model of a system may be regarded as a "black box" problem in which the box represents the system being studied (in this case a manoeuvring vessel) - see Fig. 1. If we measure the inputs and outputs to and from the box then it should be possible to deduce the contents. Fig. 2 shows the track of a VLCC in the Solent, obtained from thedolite measurements; this track is an example of the output from the "black box". The input to the system, namely the rudder angle, is shown in Fig. 3 (the engine speed was substantially constant during the manoeuvre). A mathematical model containing 16 unknown coefficients was postulated and the coefficients determined by a regression analysis using a least squares fit. The model was then programmed on a special analogue type computer and fine tuning of the coefficients carried out until the simulated output from the computer matched the actual measured response of the vessel. Figs. 4 and 5 show the final result; surge, sway and yaw velocities (u,v and r) were used in the matching process rather than the

*©IMA; Controller HMSO London, 1979

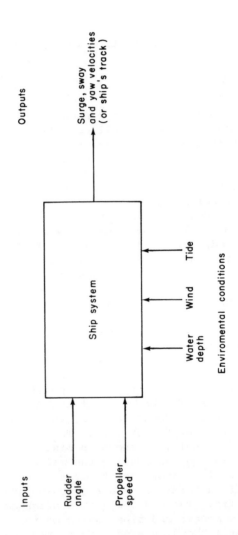

Fig. 1 Representation of a manoeuvring ship

actual track of the ship. Although a reasonable result was
obtained for the original manoeuvre, the model did not reproduce well other manoeuvres not used in the original identification process. This highlights a major hazard in the input-
output technique, namely that any model derived will generally
only be valid within the range of inputs and outputs used to
determine the model. It should be noted that in the above
example, used to illustrate the method, some additional information was used - the structure of the model was postulated from
a previous knowledge of ship manoeuvring and hence total reliance was not placed on the input-output relationship.

There is however an alternative way of solving the "black
box" problem; we can look inside the box and carry out suitable
measurements on the contents. For example, we could measure
the force produced by the rudder on a ship when moved through
an angle, or the thrust produced by the propeller. The hydrodynamic forces and moments acting on the ship due to sideslip
and turning and combinations of these must also be measured.
The summation of all the various forces and moments acting on
the ship should enable a complete mathematical model to be
formed. Unfortunately, the measurements required are such
that it is impractical to carry them out on a full-scale ship.
A physical model of the vessel must therefore be used and the
scaling of the results from model to full-scale is a well established and fairly well proven procedure. This latter technique of studing the inside of the box is generally preferable
where feasible because a better understanding of the system
is obtained and the mathematical model can generally be extra-
polated to some extent outside the range of measurements used
to determine it. However the method does have limitations;
even using physical models it is impractical to make all the
required measurements due to the large number of variables.
Some of the inevitable approximations may result in the mathematical model not reproducing the ship manoeuvring behaviour
as precisely as might be required. In this respect the input-
output method has the advantage in that a best fit is obtained
in terms of actual manoeuvring behaviour.

At the National Maritime Institute the approach has been
to combine both methods in a hybrid technique, thereby exploit-
ing the advantage of both methods. This represents a major
difference from previous mathematical models which have been
determined using one or other of the methods above. The NMI
procedure can be summarised as follows:

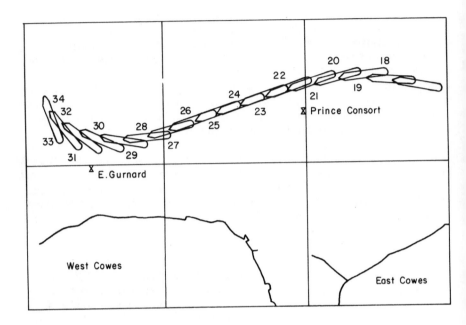

Fig. 2   Track of the VLCC "Esso Rotterdam" in the Šolent

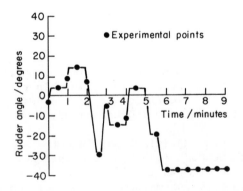

Fig. 3   Time history of rudder angle, "Esso Rotterdam"

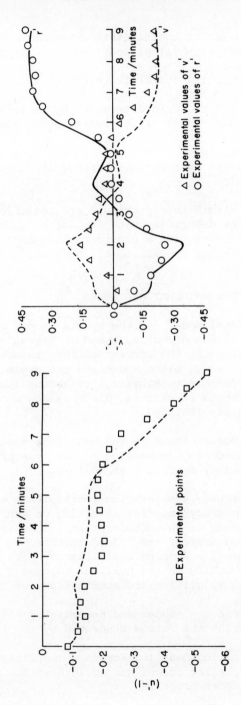

Fig. 4 Comparison of simulated and measured non-dimensional surge (u′), sway (v′) and yaw (r′) velocities, "Esso Rotterdam"

(i)   limited number of coefficients determined by direct
        measurements on physical model of ship (constrained
        model tests),
(ii)   some of remaining coefficients estimated using empirical
        data,
(iii)   remaining coefficients determined by regression analysis
        on input-output data (free running model tests or full-
        scale data),
(iv)   coefficients tuned manually on an analogue computer or
        its equivalent to reproduce correct input-output
        relationship.

Large variations within this procedure are possible. The
general model to be described, with its large number of coeffi-
cents, will normally require a considerable amount of work
under (i). The simpler special model, however, might dispense
with (i) altogether.

2. STRUCTURE OF THE MATHEMATICAL MODEL

Both the general model and the special model consist of
three coupled equations of motion based on Newton's 2nd law.
These equations describe the forces and moments acting in the
horizontal plane. Roll, pitch and heave are neglected. Force
equations are preferable to kinematic relationships because
they allow the effects of external disturbances such as wind
and tugs to be easily included.

The various coefficients in the equations can be divided
into four main categories, depending on the type of force
(or moment) which they describe, as follows:

(i)   Inertia Forces - acceleration coefficients which des-
        cribe the hydrodynamic forces acting on the hull due
        to surge, sway or yaw accelerations; sometimes referred
        to as "added masses" and "added inertia."
(ii)   Damping Forces - damping coefficients which describe
        the forces acting on the hull due to steady surge,
        sway or yaw velocities and combinations of these
        velocities.
(iii)   Exciting Forces - rudder and propeller coefficients
        which describe the forces generated by the rudder and
        propeller.
(iv)   Damping/Exciting Coupling Forces - coefficients which
        describe coupling forces due to interaction between
        hull and rudder/propeller.

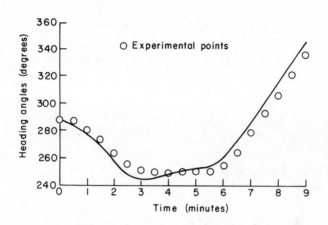

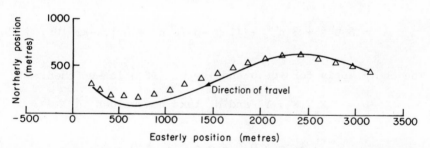

Fig. 5   Comparison of simulated and measured heading angle
         and track, "Esso Rotterdam"

2.1   General Model

The general model consists of the following three equations of motion expressed in body axes with the origin at the centre of gravity of the vessel (see nomenclature in section 9 and sign convention in Fig. 16).

$$O = X_1 U'^2 + (X_2 +m^*)v' r' + X_3 \lambda_1 \delta^2 + X_4 v'^2 + X_5 r'^2$$

$$+ X_6 U' n' + X_7 n'^2 + (X_8 -m^*)\overset{\bullet}{u'} \qquad (1)$$

$$O = Y_1 v' U' + (Y_2 -m^*)r' U' + Y_3 \lambda_2 \delta + Y_4 v' |v'| + (Y_5 +m^*/_2)\frac{v'^2 r'}{U'}$$

$$+ Y_6 \frac{v' r'^2}{U'} + Y_7 n'^2 + (Y_8 -m^*)\overset{\bullet}{v'} + Y_9 \overset{\bullet}{r'} \qquad (2)$$

$$O = N_1 v' U' + N_2 r' U' + N_3 \lambda_2 \delta + N_4 v' |v'| + N_5 \frac{v'^2 r'}{U'}$$

$$+ N_6 \frac{v' r'^2}{U'} + N_7 n'^2 + N_8 \overset{\bullet}{v'} + (N_9 -I^*_{zz})\overset{\bullet}{r'} \qquad (3)$$

where
$$\lambda_1 = \alpha_1 U'^2 + \alpha_2 n'^2 +(1-\alpha_1 -\alpha_2)U' n' \qquad (4)$$

$$\lambda_2 = \beta_1 U'^2 + \beta_2 n'^2 + (1-\beta_1 -\beta_2)U' n' + \beta_3 |v' -kr'| U' . \qquad (5)$$

The above apply for +ve u and +ve n. If n is -ve then:

$$X_6, X_7, Y_7 \text{ and } N_7 \text{ take new values}$$

$$\lambda_1 = \alpha_1 U'^2 + \alpha_4 n'^2 (\lambda_1 \not\gtrless 0) \qquad (6)$$

$$\lambda_2 = \beta_1 U'^2 + \beta_3 |v' - kr'| U' + \beta_4 n'^2 (\lambda_2 \not\gtrless 0) \qquad (7)$$

The inertial terms mvr (X equation) and -mur (Y equation) appear as $m^*v' r'$ in the X equation and $-m^*r' U' + \frac{1}{2} m^*\frac{v'^2 r'}{U'}$ in the Y equation. The latter involves the approximation: $\sqrt{1-(v' /U')^2} \approx 1- \frac{1}{2} (v' /U')^2$ (v' is small compared with U').

This is done for convenience so that no terms involving u' appear ($\overset{\cdot}{u}'$ does however appear in the X equation).

The various terms in equations (1) to (7) have been selected from a combination of theoretical considerations and experimental data. Many of the theoretical considerations have been described well by Abkowitz (1964) and Norrbin (1971). Some of the more important considerations may be summarised as follows:

(i)   port and starboard symmetry results in the X equation containing only even functions of v and r and the Y and N equations containing only odd functions of v and r;

(ii)   only linear acceleration terms appear and cross-coupling between velocity and acceleration is neglected (non-linear and cross-coupling terms are absent from the potential flow solution and acceleration terms are essentially the result of the inertia of the fluid);

(iii) terms higher than third order are set to zero.

In the set of equations (1) to (7) all the hull damping coefficients (except X_1) relate to the vessel with rudder amidships and propeller speed corresponding to self-propulsion. Departures from this condition are catered for by the rudder/propeller coefficients. The coefficients X_4, Y_4 and N_4 and the expressions for λ_1 and λ_2 have all been formulated from experimental data obtained by constrained oblique tow tests on a number of hull forms. The choice of the remaining non-linear terms X_5, Y_5, Y_6, N_5 and N_6 has been based on the results of constrained model tests using a rotating arm together with free running model tests. The various techniques of testing, measurement and analysis using constrained models and free running models form a considerable subject and it is not intended to describe these techniques any further in this paper. Burcher (1972) has described the oblique tow test, rotating arm test and planar motion mechanism test; all three of these constrained test techniques in addition to the use of free running models have been used in the formulation of equations (1) to (7). However, adapting the procedure outlined in the introduction, coefficient values for a new ship type may often be adequately determined using only the simplest and cheapest techniques, namely oblique tow and free running test.

2.2 Special Model

The expressions for λ_1 and λ_2 in the general model arise
from the need to describe accurately the rudder forces over a
wide range of operating conditions, these forces being very
sensitive to changes in both forward speed and propeller speed
If however we place the restriction that the engine speed is
constant or varies only gradually, then with the ship travelling in a straight line:

$$U' = n' \text{ so that } \lambda_1 = \lambda_2 = U'^2.$$

When the ship enters a turn and loses speed U' and n' will no
longer be equal, but the consequent effect on the rudder force
can be allowed for by modifying the damping coefficients. If
at the same time we reduce the number of non-linear terms then
a considerably simpler mathematical model is obtained:

$$0 = X_1 U'^2 + (X_2 + m^*) v' r' + X_3 U'^2 \delta^2 + X_6 U' n' + X_7 n'^2$$

$$+ (X_8 - m^*) \dot{u}' \tag{8}$$

$$0 = Y_1 v' U' + (Y_2 - m^*) r' U' + Y_3 U'^2 \delta + (Y_5 + m^*/_2) \frac{v'^2 r'}{U'}$$

$$+ Y_7 n'^2 + (Y_8 - m^*) \dot{v}' + Y_9 \dot{r}' \tag{9}$$

$$0 = N_1 v' U' + N_2 r' U' + N_3 U'^2 \delta + N_7 n'^2 + N_8 \dot{v}'$$

$$+ (N_9 - I^*_{zz}) \dot{r}'. \tag{10}$$

The non-linear damping term Y_5 has been retained in preference to the other non-linear terms because it has been
found to be the most significant. It should be noted that the
coefficient values in both models are obtained by determining
the best fit to experimental data. The values determined are
therefore dependent upon the structure of the mathematical
model since the setting of high order terms to zero distorts
the remaining terms. The coefficient values in the special
model are not therefore necessarily the same as those in the
general model (for the same vessel), notwithstanding the

modifications due to the rudder forces referred to earlier.

With estimates of the acceleration coefficients X_8, Y_8 and N_9 (for example from Motora (1960)) and estimates of the resistance and bollard pull coefficients, X_1 and X_7, the remaining coefficient values in the special model can be identified directly from standard full-scale manoeuvring trials. The only additional requirement is that some measurements of drift angle and speed are made during the spiral test in addition to the usual measurement of turning rate and rudder angle. Using published results of the "Esso Bernica" manoeuvring trials Clarke *et al.* (1973), I demonstrated the technique in a previous paper (Gill (1976)) from which Figs. 6 and 7 are taken. They show a comparison of simulated and measured results for a Bech reverse spiral test and a $20°/20°$ Kempf manoeuvre. This demonstrates that the special model, even with only one principal non-linear term Y_5, is able to represent the highly non-linear behaviour of a dynamically unstable vessel.

3. ENVIRONMENTAL CONDITIONS

The manoeuvring behaviour of a vessel is dependent on water depth (when this is less than about 3 x ship's draught), wind and tide - see Fig. 1. The effects of each of these can be represented in the mathematical model as described below.

3.1 Water depth

When the water depth is less than about 3 x ship's draught, all the coefficient values in the mathematical model become dependent on water depth. Some coefficients show a very marked variation particularly when the depth to draught ratio is less than about 1.5. The procedure at NMI is to determine coefficient values for deepwater and 4 shallow water depths. Coefficient values for intermediate depths are then obtained by interpolation. Results of tests to determine the acceleration coefficients and linear damping coefficients for two hull forms in a range of water depths are given in Gill and Price (1977).

3.2 Wind

The effects of wind can be represented by adding to the R.H.S. of equations (1), (2) and (3) or equations (8), (9),

(10), non-dimensional wind forces and moment X_W, Y_W and N_W. These can generally be adequately defined by the following expressions:

$$X_W = W_R'^2 a_1 \cos\theta$$

$$Y_W = W_R'^2 b_1 \sin\theta$$

$$N_W = W_R'^2 (c_1 \sin\theta + c_2 \sin2\theta)$$

where W_R' is the non-dimensional relative wind speed and θ is the angle between the ship's head and the relative wind. The coefficients a_1, b_1, c_1 and c_2 are determined from wind tunnel tests on an above water model of the vessel, or from estimated values, obtained for example from the collected data given by Gould (1967).

3.3 Tide

A steady uniform horizontal current has no effect on the manoeuvres of a ship except to produce a stady shift of position superimposed on the zero current path. This may appear surprising but it can be readily proved (see Appendix I). The position and heading of the vessel including the effects of a steady current of strength V are therefore defined by the following expressions:

$$x = L_{pp} \int (u' \sin\psi + v' \cos\psi - V' \sin\gamma) dt' \quad \text{(easterly position)}$$

$$y = L_{pp} \int (u' \cos\psi - v' \sin\psi - V' \cos\gamma) dt' \quad \text{(northerly position)}$$

$$\psi = \int r' dt'$$

where ψ is the ship's heading angle and γ the current direction.

4. SPIRAL RESPONSE

To determine the coefficients and validate the mathematical model, it is necessary to calculate the spiral response of the model; this is defined by the steady rate of turn, drift angle and speed of the vessel as a function of rudder angle. It should be noted that this is not a true steady motion since the ship must continually be accelerated inward in order to pursue a curved path. The spiral response is particularly valuable because the corresponding experimental data, whether from physical model or from full-scale, generally has good accuracy, since the effects of experimental errors can be reduced by averaging the measurements over a substantial period of time.

The spiral response of the mathematical model can be determined by computer simulation in which the set of differential equations is solved until steady turning conditions are achieved, for a range of fixed rudder angles. The terms (X_8-m^*), (Y_8-m^*) and $(N_9-I_{zz}^*)$ can conveniently all be set to artifically small values so that the steady turning condition is rapidly reached with a consequent useful saving in computation time. However this method is not ideal because the reverse loop part of the spiral response of an unstable vessel will not be obtained without the use of an automatic active controller in the computer program to maintain the simulated vessel in specified rates of turn.

The alternative method of calculating the spiral response is to set the accelerations to zero in the set of equations and then solve the resulting simultaneous equations for u', v' and r' for given values of n' and δ. This method will reproduce the reverse loop characteristic of an unstable vessel. Considering the general model, we obtain the following from equations (1) to (5) after dividing throughout by u'^2 and setting $\dot{u}' = \dot{v}' = \dot{r}' = 0$:

$$0 = X_1 + (X_2+m^*)v^*r^* + X_3\eta_1\delta^2 + X_4v^{*2} + X_5r^{*2} + X_6n^* + X_7n^{*2} \quad (11)$$

$$0 = Y_1v^* + (Y_2-m^*)r^* + Y_3\eta_2\delta + Y_4v^*|v^*| + (Y_5+m^*/_2)v^{*2}r^*$$

$$+ Y_6v^*r^{*2} + Y_7n^{*2} \quad (12)$$

$$O = N_1 v^* + N_2 r^* + N_3 \eta_2 \delta + N_4 v^* |v^*| + N_5 v^{*2} r^*$$

$$+ N_6 v^* r^{*2} + N_7 n^{*2} \tag{13}$$

where $\quad \eta_1 = \lambda_1 / U'^2 = \alpha_1 + \alpha_2 n^{*2} + (1-\alpha_1 -\alpha_2) n^* \tag{14}$

$$\eta_2 = \lambda_2 / U'^2 = \beta_1 + \beta_2 n^* + (1-\beta_1 -\beta_2) n^*$$

$$+ \beta_3 |v^* - k r^*|. \tag{15}$$

The corresponding equations for the special model are:

$$O = X_1 + (X_2 + m^*) v^* r^* + X_3 \delta^2 + X_6 n^* + X_7 n^{*2} \tag{16}$$

$$O = Y_1 v^* + (Y_2 - m^*) r^* + Y_3 \delta + (Y_5 + m^*/_2) v^{*2} r^* + Y_7 n^{*2} \tag{17}$$

$$O = N_1 v^* + N_2 r^* + N_3 \delta + N_7 n^{*2}. \tag{18}$$

The solution of the set of simultaneous equations (11) to
(15) or (16) to (18) yields values of n^*, v^* and r^* for a
range of values of δ. U' can then be determined for a given
value of n' and thence v' and r' are found, thus defining the
spiral response.

The only asymmetric terms in both the general model and
the special model are Y_7 and N_7. These coefficients describe
the lateral thrust produced by the propeller of a single screw
vessel which results in different turning characteristics to
port and starboard. The solution of the set of simultaneous
equations (11) to (15) or (16) to (18) is made significantly
easier if Y_7 and N_7 are set to zero so that the equations are
symmetric and therefore produce identical turning characteristics to port and starboard. This has been done for the
"Esso Bernicia" in Fig. 6. An alternative method of represen-
ing the turning asymmetry is to set Y_7 and N_7 to zero and let
δ become a nominal rudder angle, related to the true rudder

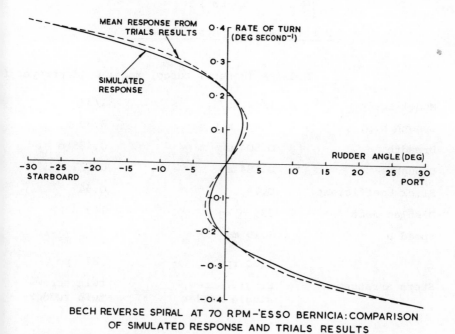

BECH REVERSE SPIRAL AT 70 RPM-'ESSO BERNICIA:COMPARISON
OF SIMULATED RESPONSE AND TRIALS RESULTS

Fig. 6   Bech reverse spiral at 70 rpm - "Esso Bernicia":
comparison of simulated response and trials results

angle, δ_a, by the expression:

$$\delta = \delta_a + k_1 |\delta_a| + k_2 . \qquad (19)$$

Although not such a good physical representation, this method
does allow the simultaneous equations to be more easily solved.
Methods of solving the simultaneous equations (11) to (15)
and (16) to (18) are given in Appendix II.

5.   GENERAL AND SPECIAL MODELS OF A CARGO VESSEL

Coefficient values have been determined using a physical
model of a general cargo vessel (hereafter referred to as
Model A). Details of Model A are given in Table I.

TABLE I

Particulars of physical models

	Model A (general cargo)	Model C (destroyer f
Model scale	1/42.057	1/33
Length b.p.	3.424 m	3.80 m
Breadth	0.504 m	0.435 m
Draught	0.184 m	0.127 m
Block Coefficient	0.74	0.54
Displacement	235.5 kg	113.4 kg
Speed U_0	1.19 ms^{-1}	0.85 ms^{-1}
n_0	1160 rpm	387 rpm
Stern arrangement	Single screw, single rudder	twin screws twin rudder

Sixteen coefficient values for the general model and eigh coefficient values for the special model were determined from simple oblique tow tests. The remaining coefficients in each model were then determined from free running model experiment: except for X_8, Y_8 and N_9 which were estimated from the data given by Motora (1960). The coefficients k_1 and k_2 have been used to reproduce turning asymmetry rather than Y_7 and N_7. Fig. 8 shows a comparison of simulated spiral response of both mathematical models with the experimentally measured spiral response of the physical model. The turning circle shown in Fig. 9 was used to find the optimum value of N_8 in the genera model. All the remaining transient tests carried out with the physical model are shown in Figs. 10 to 13 and Table II. Non of these tests was used to assist in fixing coefficient value and they therefore provide a good check on the validity of the mathematical models.

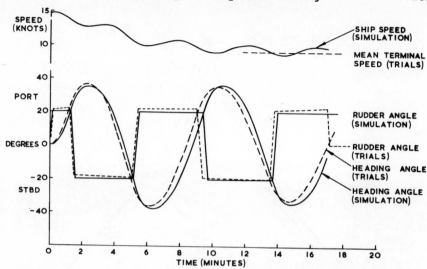

Fig. 7 20°/20° Kempf manoeuvre at 70 rpm "Esso Bernicia":
comparison of simulated response and trials response

TABLE II

Comparison of measured and predicted Kempf manoeuvres for
model A

Propeller speed (rpm)	675	960	512
Heading Change	±24°	±28°	±24°
Rudder Angle	±21½°	±21½°	±30°
Measured Period, s	48.0	41.5	50.0
Simulated Period, s (general model)	45.0	35.5	50.0
Simulated Period, s (special model)	45.5	36.0	55.0
Measured maximum heading	30.0°	36.5°	30.0°
Simulated maximum heading (general model)	31.9°	37.0°	31.3°
Simulated maximum heading (Special model)	34.5°	40.2°	36.5°

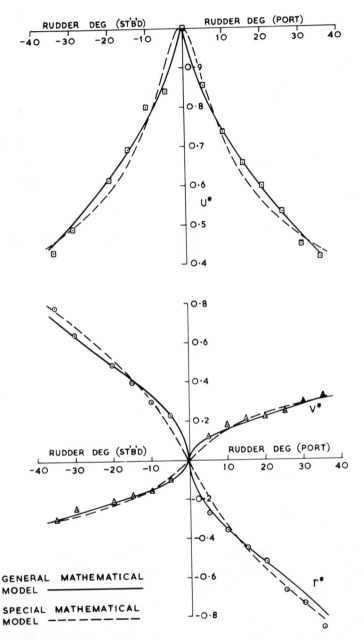

Fig. 8 Steady turning chacteristics, model 'A' at 1120 rev mi
        comparison between predicted response and experimental
        points

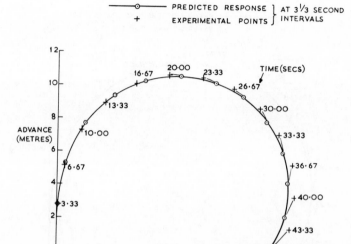

Fig. 9   Comparison of measured and simulated turning circles
using general mathematical model after optimisation
of N_8,model 'A' at 950 rpm, $22°$ starboard rudder

6.   ANALYSIS OF DYNAMIC STABILITY

In considering the dynamic stability of a vessel on a
straight course we can neglect the non-linear terms in the equations of motion since we are dealing only with small disturbances
from straight line motion. For simplicity we will take the
case when $U' = n' = 1.0$, whereupon the X equation vanishes
and the Y and N equations become (general or special model):

$$0 = Y_1 v' + (Y_2 - m^*) r' + (Y_8 - m^*) \dot{v}' + Y_9 \dot{r}' \qquad (20)$$

$$0 = N_1 v' + N_2 r' + N_8 \dot{v}' + (N_9 - I^*_{zz}) \dot{r}' \qquad (21)$$

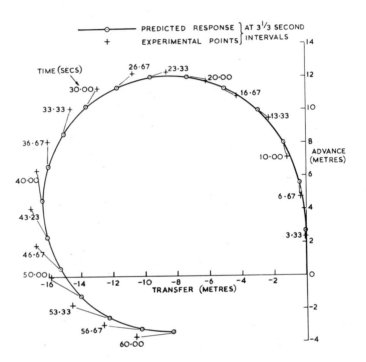

Fig. 10   Comparison of measured and predicted turning circles
          using general mathematical model, model 'A' at 940 r[
          15° port rudder

noting that the rudder is held amidships so that $\delta = 0$.
Eliminating v' and its derivative we obtain the following
second order differential equation:

$$A\ddot{r}' + B\dot{r}' + Cr' = 0 \tag{22}$$

$$\text{where } A = (Y_8 - m^*)(N_9 - I_{zz}^*) - Y_9 N_8 \tag{23}$$

$$B = Y_1(N_9 - I_{zz}^*) - Y_9 N_1 + (Y_8 - m^*)N_2 - (Y_2 - m^*)N_8 \tag{24}$$

$$C = Y_1 N_2 - (Y_2 - m^*)N_1 \ . \tag{25}$$

Modelling of Ship Manoeuvring   213

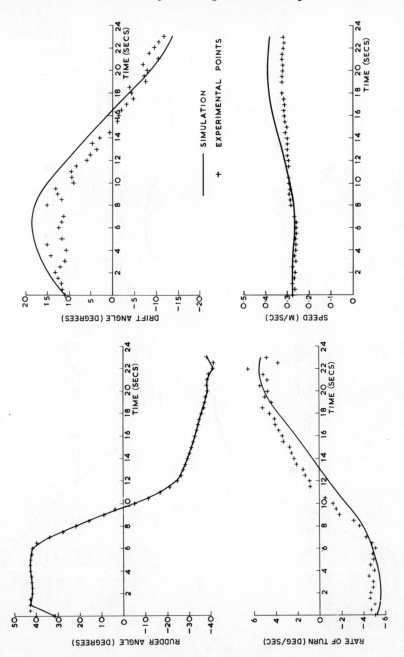

Fig. 11   Comparison of measured and predicted responses using
general mathematical model, model 'A' at 1030 rpm

H

Gill

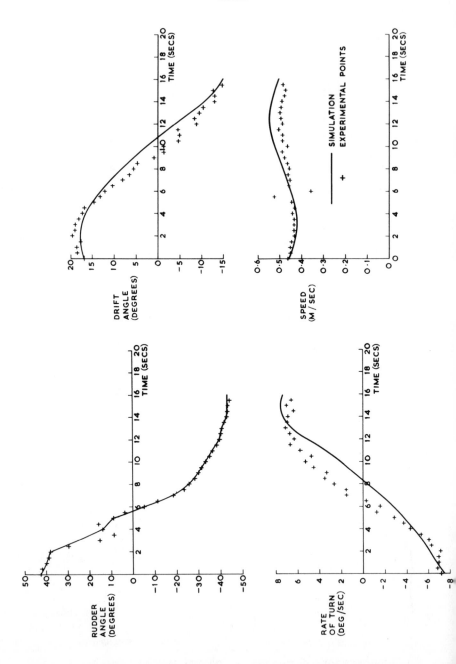

Fig. 12   Comparison of measured and predicted responses using
         general mathematical model, model 'A' at 910 rpm

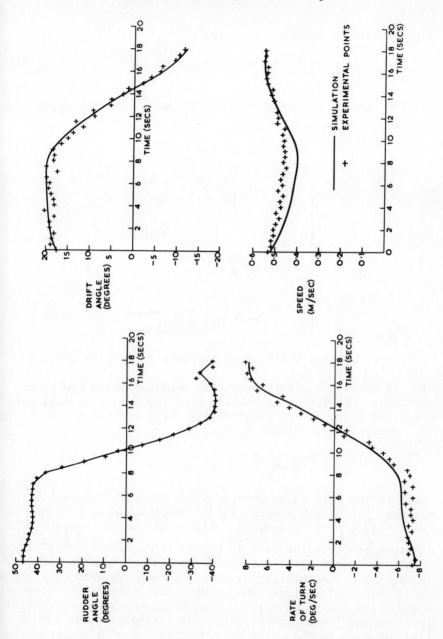

Fig. 13   Comparison of measured and predicted responses using
general mathematical model, model 'A' at 707 rpm

The solution of equation (22) is:

$$r' = d_1 e^{\tau_1 t'} + d_2 e^{\tau_2 t'} \tag{26}$$

where d_1 and d_2 are constants and τ_1 and τ_2 are the roots of:

$$A\tau^2 + B\tau + C = 0 \tag{27}$$

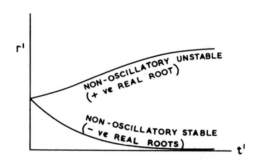

Fig. 14   Non-oscillatory response to disturbance

Fig. 14 shows the possible dynamic behaviour when the roots
are real. For dynamic stability both roots must be negative.
Now A and B are always positive for ships so that the condition
for negative roots is C > O, i.e.:

$$Y_1 N_2 - (Y_2 - m^*) N_1 > O$$

which is the well known condition for dynamic stability.
Hitherto the possible existence of complex conjugate roots has
not normally been considered. The condition for complex conjugate roots to exist is that $B^2 - 4AC$ is negative. This will
result in an oscillatory response to a disturbance as shown
in Fig. 15. The oscillatory unstable response cannot exist
for a ship (using linear theory with small disturbances) because
A and B are always positive. However the oscillatory stable
response can theoretically exist for a ship. At NMI a hull
form has been tested which in a certain range of water depths
has measured coefficient values which result in complex conjugate roots. The actual measurements on the hull form (denoted
Model C) have been published by Gill and Price (1977). Particular
of Model C are given in Table I and the coefficient values

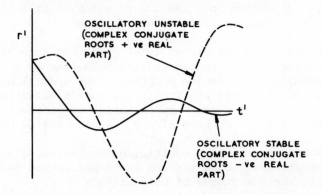

Fig. 15   Oscillatory response to disturbance

obtained at a depth to draught ratio of 2.0 are as follows ($\times 10^3$):
Y_1 - 16.4; Y_2 -m* - 0.4; Y_8 -m* - 8.0; Y_9 - 0.9; N_1 - 2.9;

N_2 - 0.95; N_8 + 0.2; N_9 -I^*_{zz} - 0.26.   At this depth the roots

of equation (27) are complex conjugate. The corresponding
values of A, B and C in equations (22) and (27) are
A = 2.26, B = 9.33 and C = 14.42 which give complex conjugate
roots. The predicted oscillatory stability will have a non-
dimensional frequency of ω*, where:

$$\omega^* = \sqrt{\frac{C}{A} - \left\{\frac{B}{2A}\right\}^2} = 1.46 \ .$$

This represents a period of 20.1 seconds at the speed of
0.85 ms^{-1} used when measuring the coefficients. Unfortunately
the long period of the oscillations makes experimental verifi-
cation of this predicted oscillatory behaviour a rather difficult task. The corresponding period for the full-scale vessel
is 1.92 minutes at a speed of 9.5 knots.

7. CONCLUSIONS

(i) Since no exact mathematical model of a manoeuvring ship
is possible in practice and approximations must be made, there
are considerable advantages in adopting a flexible approach
both to the structure of the model and the methods of determining coefficient values. The most efficient model can then

be selected depending upon the use to which it will be put
and the data available for its determination.

(ii) The general mathematical model described here gives a
good approximation of the manoeuvring behaviour of a vessel
for ship handling simulation purposes. The special model also
described can be determined from full-scale manoeuvring trials
if desired and gives a good approximation of manoeuvring behaviour for constant or only slowly changing engine speed.

(iii) The determination of coefficient values using a combination of constrained model testing and input-output technique
can exploit the advantages of both methods.

(iv) In addition to the well known non-oscillatory dynamically
stable and unstable characteristics, there can also exist in
ships an oscillatory stable behaviour.

8.   ACKNOWLEDGEMENT

     The assistance of members of staff of NMI with the experi-
mental work, particularly Mr. W. Sims, is gratefully acknow-
ledged. The paper is published by permission of the Director
of the National Maritime Institute.

9.   NOMENCLATURE

     The sign convention is shown in Fig. 16.

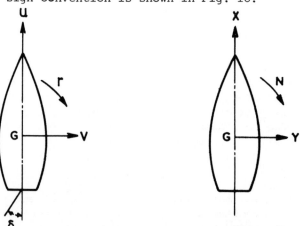

Fig. 16 Sign convention. Positive directions as shown

a_1 wind force coefficient

b_1 wind force coefficient

c_i wind moment coefficient

I_{zz} moment of inertia in yaw

I_{zz}^{*} $I_{zz}/\tfrac{1}{2}\rho L_{pp}^{5}$

k_i rudder coefficient

L_{pp} ship length between perpendiculars

m ship mass

m^{*} $m/\tfrac{1}{2}\rho L_{pp}^{3}$

N yaw moment

N_i yaw moment coefficient

n propeller speed

n_o reference propeller speed

n' n/n_o

n^{*} n'/U'

r yaw rate

r' rL_{pp}/U_o

r^{*} rL_{pp}/U

$\dot{r}'$ dr'/dt'

$\ddot{r}'$ dr'^{2}/dt'^{2}

t' (real time) x U_o/L_{pp}

U track speed = $\sqrt{u^2+v^2}$

U_o reference speed

U' U/U_o

$U*$ $U'/n' = {}^1/n*$

u surge velocity

u' u/U_o

$\dot{u}'$ du'/dt'

V current velocity

V' V/U_o

v sway velocity

v' v/U_o

$v*$ v/U

$\dot{v}'$ dv'/dt'

W_R relative wind speed

$W_{R'}$ W_R/U_o

X surge force

X_i surge force coefficient

x easterly position

Y sway force

Y_i sway force coefficient

y northerly position

α_i rudder coefficient (surge)

β_i rudder coefficent (sway and yaw)

γ current direction

δ nominal rudder angle

δ_a true rudder angle

η_i rudder parameter

θ angle between ship's head and relative wind

λ_i rudder parameter

ρ mass density of water

ϕ angle between ship's head and current

ψ heading angle

ω frequency of sway and yaw oscillatory response

ω^* $\omega L_{pp}/U$

10. REFERENCES

Abkowitz, M. A. "Lectures on ship hydrodynamics - steering manoeuvrability", HyA Report No. HY-5, 1964.

Burcher, R. K. "Developments in ship manoeuvrability", *Trans. RINA,* Vol. **114**, 1972, pp. 1-32.

Clarke, D., Paterson, D. R. and Wooderson, R. K. "Manoeuvring trials with the 193,000 tonne d.w. tanker "ESSO BERNICIA", *Trans. RINA,* Vol. **115**, 1973, pp. 89-109.

Gill, A. D. "The identification of manoeuvring equations from ship trial results", *Trans. RINA,* Vol. **118**, 1976, pp. 145-157.

Gill, A. D. and Price, W. G. "Experimental evaluation of the effects of water depth and speed on the manoeuvring derivatives of ship models", RINA paper W3 (1977) to appear in *Trans. RINA.*

Gould, R. W. F. "Measurements of the wind forces on a series of models of merchant ships", NPL Aero Report 1233, April 1967.

Motora, S. "On the measurement of added mass and added moment of inertia of ships in steering motion", Proc. First Symposium on Ship Manoeuvrability, Washington 1960, DTMB Report 1461, 1960.

Norrbin, N. H. "Theory and observations on the use of a mathematical model for ship manoeuvring in deep and confined waters", Publication of the Swedish State Shipbuilding Experimental Tank, (SSPA), No. 68, 1971.

APPENDIX I

EQUATIONS OF MOTION FOR A SHIP MOVING IN A CURRENT

In still water the equations of motion for a ship are as follows, using body axes:

$$
\left.
\begin{array}{l}
m(\dot{u}-rv) = X(u,v,r,\dot{u},\dot{v},\dot{r} \ \ldots) \\[2ex]
m(\dot{v}+ur) = Y(u,v,r,\dot{u},\dot{v},\dot{r} \ \ldots) \\[2ex]
I_{zz}\dot{r} = N(u,v,r,\dot{u},\dot{v},\dot{r} \ \ldots)
\end{array}
\right\}
\qquad (i)
$$

The R.H.S. of these equations represent the hydrodynamic forces on the hull; u,v and r are the velocities in surge, sway and yaw relative to earth, and dots denote differentiation w.r.t. time.

Now introduce a steady current of velocity V (see Fig. 17).

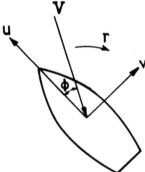

Fig. 17   Ship moving in a current of velocity v

Let u_c and v_c be the velocities of the ship relative to water in surge and sway. The hydrodynamic forces on the hull will now depend on the velocities u_c, v_c and r and their derivative Hence the equations become:

$$m(\dot{u}-rv) = X(u_c, v_c, r, \dot{u}_c, \dot{v}_c, \dot{r} \ldots)$$

$$m(\dot{v}+ur) = Y(u_c, v_c, r, \dot{u}_c, \dot{v}_c, \dot{r} \ldots)$$

$$I_{zz}\dot{r} = N(u_c, v_c, r, \dot{u}_c, \dot{v}_c, \dot{r} \ldots)$$

(ii)

Now $u = u_c - V\cos\phi$

and $v = v_c - V\sin\phi$

(iii)

hence $\dot{u} = \dot{u}_c - \dot{V}\cos\phi + V\dot{\phi}\sin\phi$

and $\dot{v} = \dot{v}_c - \dot{V}\sin\phi - V\dot{\phi}\cos\phi$.

For a steady current $\dot{V} = 0$ and $\dot{\phi} = -r$,

hence $\dot{u} = \dot{u}_c - Vr\sin\phi$

and $\dot{v} = \dot{v}_c + Vr\cos\phi$.

(iv)

Substituting equations (iii) and (iv) into equations (ii) we obtain:

$$m\left[\dot{u}_c - Vr\sin\phi - r(v_c - V\sin\phi) \right] = X(u_c, v_c, r \ldots)$$

i.e. $m(\dot{u}_c - rv_c) = X(u_c, v_c, r, \dot{u}_c, \dot{v}_c, \dot{r})$

similarly $m(\dot{v}_c + u_c r) = Y(u_c, v_c, r, \dot{u}_c, \dot{v}_c, \dot{r})$

$$I_{zz}\dot{r} = N(u_c, v_c, r, \dot{u}_c, \dot{v}_c, \dot{r})$$.

(v)

Now the set of equations (v) are identical to the set (i) for still water, except that u and v and their derivatives are replaced by u_c and v_c and their derivatives. The effect of a steady current on a manoeuvring ship is therefore a steady shift of position superimposed on the zero current path.

APPENDIX II

THE SPIRAL RESPONSE OF THE MATHEMATICAL MODEL

1. General Model

    We wish to solve the set of simultaneous equations (11) to (15) to obtain the spiral response for any specified propeller speed, for a given set of coefficient values X_i, Y_i, N_i, α_i, β_i. Instead of solving the equations for various values of δ, a better approach is to take assumed values of v* and solve in reverse for δ. This latter method is particularly advantageous when considering a dynamically unstable vessel, where for small values of δ there are three sets of possible values for speed, rate of turn and drift angle (see Fig. 18). Solving in reverse for δ using assumed values of v* avoids this problem of handling three real roots over part of the spiral response, because for each value of drift angle (or rate of turn) there is only one correct value of rudder angle.

    Adopting this "reverse" method of solution, we first set $Y_7 = N_7 = 0$. Then taking an assumed value of v* we solve equations (12) and (13) for r* by eliminating $\eta_2\delta$. This yields a quadratic equation in r*, and of the two roots, only one (the root of the greater magnitude) is meaningful. Using this root we calculate $\eta_2\delta$ and then substituting the values for v*, r* and $\eta_2\delta$ into equation (11) we obtain the following equation:

$$0 = X_R + X_6 n^* + X_7 n^{*2} + X_3 \frac{\eta_1 \chi^2}{\eta_2{}^2} \tag{28}$$

where $\chi = \eta_2\delta$ and $X_R = X_1 + (X_2 + m^*)v^*r^* + X_4 v^{*2} + X_5 r^{*2}$.

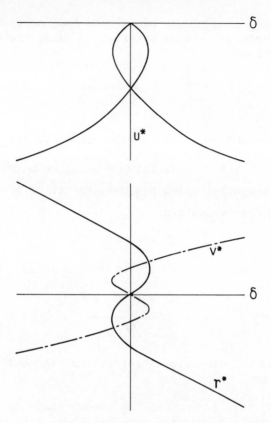

Fig. 18   Typical steady turning characteristics of an unstable
vessel

Now in equation (28) the only unknowns are n*, η_1 and η_2.
Substituting the expressions for η_1 and η_2 (equations (14 and
(15)) into equation (28) gives a sixth order equation in n*
in which n* is the only unknown. Now an algebraic equation
of the fifth or higher degree cannot be solved by rational
processes and explicit root extractions; a numerical solution
must be used. The sixth order equation in n* will in general
have six roots, but there exists only one meaningful real root,
because even for an unstable vessel there is only one value
of n* associated with a particular value of v*. This root
can be determined by Newton's method providing that an estimate
of the root can be made which is accurate enough to ensure
convergence to this root rather than to one of the other five

roots. For conventional vessels in deep or shallow water, the required root can be obtained by using the following initial estimate:

$$n^* \; \approx \; \frac{1}{(1-2|v^*|)} \; .$$

Having obtained an accurate value of n^* we can calculate η_2 and then $\delta = \chi/\eta_2$. Equation (19) can then be solved to give δ_a. The propeller speed has been specified so that n' is known and then we obtain:

$$U' = n'/n^*$$

$$v' = v^* . U'$$

$$r' = r^* . U'$$

$$u' = \sqrt{U'^2 - v'^2}$$

from which the dimensional velocities can readily be determine if required.

Using this technique, the steady state equations can be solved rapidly by digital computer for a full range of possib values of v^* (+0.4 to -0.4 in steps of 0.02 will normally be sufficient), thus defining the spiral response of the mathematical model. This can then be compared with the measur spiral response of the physical model.

Note that the above method can only produce the symmetri spiral response (with Y_7 and N_7 zero), i.e. the mean of port and starboard turning behaviour. However this can of course be compared quite satisfactorily with the mean of the port and starboard experimental results and thus provide validatio for all but Y_7 and N_7.

2. Special Model

A similar but much simpler procedure can be used for solving the set of simultaneous equations (16) to (18). Setting $Y_7 = N_7 = 0$ and taking assumed values of v^* we can solve (17) and (18) for r* and δ. Substituting values of v*, r* and δ into equation (16) yields a quadratic equation in n*:

$$0 = X_S + X_6 n^* + X_7 n^{*2} \qquad (29)$$

where $X_S = X_1 + (X_2 + m^*)v^*r^* + X_3 \delta^2$.

The meaningful root of equation (29) is:

$$n^* = \frac{-X_6 + \sqrt{X_6^2 - 4X_S X_7}}{2X_7} \ .$$

The remaining parameters can then be determined as indicated before for the general model.

COMPUTER PROGRAMS FOR COLLISION AVOIDANCE AND TRACK KEEPING

J. Kearon

(The Salvage Association)

1. INTRODUCTION

One of the first means of transport known to man was
travel by sea. This has evolved from dug-out trees and rafts
made from reeds, to ships such as the QE2 and the half million
ton tanker. During this time the work done by the personnel
on board has also changed; we have gone through the stages
of rowing, sailing, shovelling coal and lately steering
(except in docking).

Engine rooms have become, or are in the process of becoming, unmanned, and on many ships engine movements are
handled from the bridge. Apart from the cook, the only person
on board ship whose job has not changed throughout this period
is the navigator. His job has hardly changed since the days
of the first canoe, as even then his prime function was to
get from A to B as fast as possible and to avoid collisions
and strandings, which he has done very successfully.

It has been said that the art of navigating a ship requires
long experience and instant decisions based on this experience.
We can say that the function of a navigator is to collect
information, analyse and process it, and then apply the
necessary corrections. These functions are, however, those
for which a computer is also well suited. If now we prepare
various formats to determine the solution to problems encountered in manoeuvring and navigation and store them in a computer
we should be able to retrieve the desired format at the right
time. If enough formats are stored we should be able to
achieve the same standard of navigation as an expert "Ship
Master".

An analysis of the "Marine Casualty Report Scheme" by
the Chamber of Shipping of the UK says that most collisions
result from failure to avoid close quarter situations.

229

For collisions in fog the prime causes of this failure
are given as:

1. too low radar range,
2. incorrect alignment,
3. failure to observe the radar,
4. failure to appreciate the limitations of the unstabilised
    display,
5. failure to take the appropriate timely manoeuvring action
in the light of the information provided by the plot.

For collisions in clear weather the prime causes are
given as:

1. failure to keep a good lookout,
2. allowing vessels to get so close that interaction made
collision inevitable,
3. not obeying the steering rules.

From this it is clear that the basic problem is human
and would disappear with the intervention of a computer,
provided the program was based on the collision regulations.

2. A COLLISION AVOIDANCE PROGRAM

As will be appreciated, a radar no matter how sophisticated can only give range and bearing of a target at a
specific instant of time, so before we can learn anything
about the target we must solve a vector triangle. The radar
can give us the relative vector which is the sum of the target's vector and our ship's vector. It is relatively simple
to construct and solve the basic vector triangle manually,
but clearly if we are going to use a computer, we must be
able to solve and manipulate the triangle mathematically.

Fig. 1 represents the "own ship's" radar screen centred
at O, with the trace of a target ship at $T(x, y)$ at time t,
and at $A(x_1, y_1)$ at a later time $(t+t_1)$. If the target had
been stopped at time t, its trace would have moved to z by
time $(t+t_1)$.

With the angles shown we see that

$$\tan \phi = \frac{y - y_1}{x - x_1} \text{ and } \tan \alpha = \frac{y_1}{x_1} , \text{ giving}$$

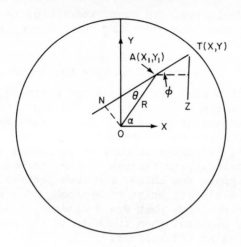

Fig. 1

$$\theta = \alpha - \phi = \arctan \left(\frac{\tan \alpha - \tan \phi}{1 + \tan \alpha \tan \phi} \right) .$$

The closest point of approach of the target, O N, is given by R sin θ where R = O A, and the time to the closest point of approach by t_1 $(\frac{R \cos \theta}{AT})$ where

$$AT = \left[(x - x_1)^2 + (y - y_1)^2 \right]^{\frac{1}{2}}.$$

In the program special arrangements must be made to deal with the situation when x = x_1.

In a multiship encounter, it is highly unlikely that three, or more, ships will arrive at the same position simultaneously. They will probably be in chronological order which means that one of the targets must constitute the greatest danger. It is clear that the element of danger does not just depend on the time of closest approach (TCPA), but also on the closest point of approach (CPA). The extent to which these factors influence the action taken by an officer on watch depends to a large degree on the importance the officer attaches to time or distance, and also on the type of ship involved. For example one officer might feel that a collision in 20 minutes constitutes a greater danger than a nearest approach

of ½ mile in 10 minutes. We must, therefore, take both
factors into account when deciding which target is most
dangerous.

One way of doing this is to take the lowest value of
$[(a \times CPA)^2 + (b \times TCPA)^2]$, where a and b depend on the importance the operator places on the CPA and TCPA. After examining numerous situations it was decided to take values of
a = 5 and b = 0.5 for the starboard sector, and a = 5 and
b = 1 elsewhere. It was necessary to introduce this distinction, to give priority to targets in the starboard sector.
For example, suppose two ships, one from port and one from
starboard, had a closest point of approach of zero miles, if
the TCPA of the one from port was 5 minutes, and the one from
starboard was 9 minutes, then the ship in the starboard sector
would be rated as more dangerous.

Using the above formula, the computer examines the targets, and decides which is the most dangerous. The CPA and
TCPA of this target are then checked to see if any action is
needed, the decision depending on which sector the target is
in.

The values of the minimum acceptable CPA and TCPA could
be input to the computer as data, but for ease of programming
these values were inserted as part of the program. We see
from Fig. 2 that these values depend upon which quadrant the
target is in; I feel they are about right, others might feel
differently.

Considering the starboard quarter, no action is needed
if the target is more than 7 miles away, or the time of nearest
approach is greater than 25 minutes. In the port quadrant,
no action is needed unless the target is having a nearest
approach of less than 1.6 miles in less than 10 minutes. For
targets overtaking, the desired nearest approach is reduced
to 1 mile (from recent experience of vessels overtaking in
traffic lanes, this 1 mile limit may have to be reduced even
further), but the time of 10 minutes could be retained.

Having ascertained whether action is needed or not, the
computer either reports that no action is needed, or goes
on to determine what action to take, or to advise.

Again the technique used is the same as that an experience
officer would take in plotting, but instead of working out

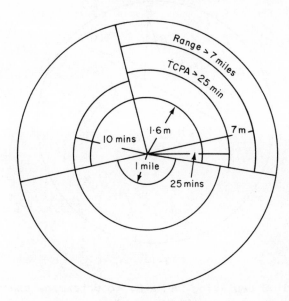

Fig. 2   CPA and TCPA diagram

the course and speed vectors manually, it is done mathematically.

Fig. 3 shows the effect that an alteration of course and/or speed has on CPA and TCPA. The alteration is assumed to be made at time t (i.e. when the trace of the target ship is at T) and to consist of a change of speed from V to V' and a turn positive to starboard through an angle β.

At time $(t+t_1)$ the trace of the target will now be at $C(x_2, y_2)$ instead of at $A(x_1, y_1)$. AB represents the displacement of "own ship" during the time from t to $(t+t_1)$ if there had been no alteration of course; CB the corresponding displacement allowing for the alteration. Hence $AB = Vt_1$ and $CB = V't_1$.

So we have $x_2 = x_1 - V't_1 \sin\beta$

$$y_2 = y_1 + Vt_1 - V't_1 \cos\beta.$$

The new track of the target ship is now along TC instead of TA. We can use the earlier formulae, with (x_2, y_2) replacing

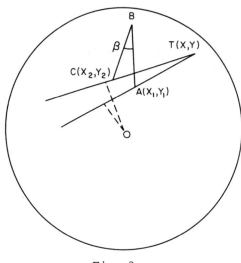

Fig. 3

(x_1, y_1) and OC replacing OA as R, to determine the new CPA
and TCPA.

No account has been taken here of the vessel's dynamic
charateristics but these could easily be inserted if known.

By repeating these calculations for other alterations of
course and/or speed the computer can determine the alteration
necessary. If none can be found the computer then reduces
the clearance distance and starts again.

Now the alteration necessary to make the CPA of one
vessel greater **than** the desired minimum could result in a
close quarter situation with another. The next stage of the
program therefore deals with multiship encounters where we
must consider the effect our alteration of course has on other
ships in the vicinity.

Having decided the alteration needed for the most dangero
target, this is tried on other targets to determine whether
any additional action is called for. If again it is not possible to find an alteration of course and speed to satisfy all
targets, the program reduces the minimum acceptable limit, and
repeats the calculations until an acceptable solution is found

The program was tested on numerous sets of encounters. Some are shown in the accompanying diagrams, together with the computer solutions (the problems are given first to enable the reader to try and solve them before looking at the solutions)

In these problems the computer has been asked if possible to give a clearance of 1.75 miles and alterations to port are discouraged in accordance with Rule 17 of the Steering Regulations.

The correct time to resume the voyage is an important feature of any collision avoidance system; course should not be resumed before it is safe but the alteration should not be held for an uneconomical length of time.

In a single ship encounter the time when it is safe to resume course can be easily calculated from the formulae. However, with an automatic system, we must consider the possibility of not being able to resume course at the calculated time because a new target is detected, or as is more likely, because one of the existing targets alter course. We must, therefore, continuously monitor all ships to detect any deterioration of the situation. Also any decision taken to resume course must be made on the situation as it is and not as it was x minutes ago. The program was therefore designed so that the computer is always trying to resume course, but will only do so when no target has a CPA of less than the desired clearance. If this is not the case, the alteration will be held until it is.

As with the first part of the program, the ranges and bearings of the targets are fed in, the computer analyses them and determines which is the most dangerous. If the CPA of this target is greater than the set limit, the computer reduces the change of course by 5 degrees. This is tested on the targets and if safe another 5 degree reduction is tried. The process is repeated until the CPA of one of the targets is less than the limit. The first half of the program then calculates the required alteration to make the situation safe again. Once back on course the computer increases speed in stages, checking each one.

The point to stress is that the computer program is designed to follow the same sequence of reasoning as an experienced ship's officer would: i.e. (a) determine if any other vessel is a danger; (b) decide what action is necessary;

(c) ensure that the proposed alteration does not bring the
vessel into close contact with a third vessel; (d) return to
course when safe.

3. A NAVIGATION PROGRAM

As with the problem of avoiding collisions, I feel that
when considering automatic navigation we should try and program
the computer to take the same action, and follow the same
procedure, that an experienced navigator would. We must,
therefore, look at the work of a navigator, and see if a
computer could be programmed to perform the task   required.
Let us see what these tasks are.

(a) At the start of a voyage, the initial course is determined
either by calculation or, as is more usual, by plotting. The
course may be either great circle or loxodromic.
(b) Having set his course, the navigator must determine the
ship's position at frequent intervals. If the vessel is
experiencing set (due to current flow), he must calculate its
magnitude, and apply a course correction to offset it.
(c) He must calculate the correction needed to regain the
course line.
(d) When an alteration point is reached he must calculate the
next course, and intiate an alteration of course.

We can see now that the navigator's task consists of
two main parts:

>   (a) calculating of course,
>   (b) following the course line.

With the navigator's job broken into its basic components
the computer program was developed along the following lines.

(a) The ship's initial position is fed in, together with speed
the distance the ship is allowed each side of the track before
being returned to the track, and the time allowed to regain
track.
(b) The course alteration points are fed in and stored; the
number of these points will depend on the storage capacity
of the computer.
(c) The initial course is calculated. The program can either
calculate the mercator course or the great circle course.
If the distance between the two points is greater than 100
miles, the great circle course is used, in which case the
computer will check the course continuously.
(d) Having set out on the initial course, the ship's position

is fed into the computer. The off-track distance is calculated,
and if it is greater than a specified distance the set angle
is calculated. This angle is then applied to counteract the
set. The computer then calculates the correction needed to
return the ship to the track. This correction is a function
of the ship's speed and the time allowed to regain the track.
The distance to the next alteration point is also calculated
and if the distance is less than a specified amount the alteration of course is calculated.

(e) A type of filter is built into the program as a safeguard
against a spurious position being fed in. If a position is
more than a certain distance off the course line, no action
is taken, but the distance is stored. This is repeated four
times, and the results checked. If all positions stored
show that the vessel is outside the limit, action would be
initiated.

It would thus be necessary to devise a system which would
feed in actual positions when they are available and, if not,
feed in dead-reckoning positions based on the ship's speed,
and course made good over the ground.

If, within the Decca or Omega coverage, positions were
continuously available the main program could receive positions
at will; if, however, only satellite fixes are available then
we must be able to determine the ship's position between
fixes. With this in mind, the computer program will calculate
the ship's position using the initial position course and
speed as parameters. If the ship was in an area where positions
could be obtained from more than one system, rather than
selecting one of the systems as the prime course, we should
use the information from all sources, apply weighting techniques, and thus determine the most likely position.

It was not possible in the time available, to include
everything. For example, an officer on watch, when considering what action to take in an encounter, must not only consider the ships but also the restrictions imposed by draft
and land. When starting to develop the program I had intended
to apply constraints such as above, by allowing the vessel to
deviate only a certain distance each side of the course line,
and the navigation program was developed with this in mind.
It was intended to join both programs together as they are,
to a large degree, inter-dependent. For example, the navigation program can only set course if safe, and the collision
avoidance program was to be restricted by navigational
restraints.

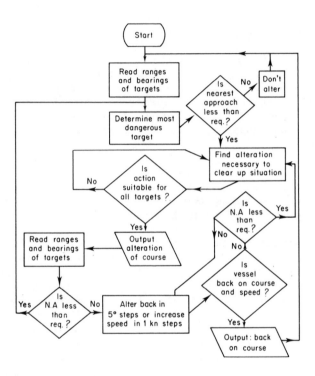

Fig. 4   Simplified flow diagram of collision avoidance progra

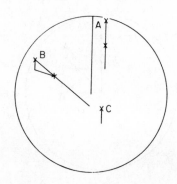

Target 'A'   N.A. 1.29 miles in 8.67 minutes.
Target 'B'   N. A. 1.14 miles in 9.57 minutes.
Target 'C'   same course and speed.

Relative Motion course 000° speed 12 knots

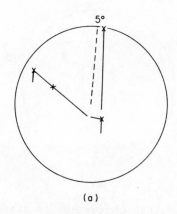

(a)

Computer solution alter 5° to starboard hold speed.
In this exercise the computer after trying combinations of
course and speed had to reduce the clearance limit

Relative motion after alteration of course.

Fig. 5(a)

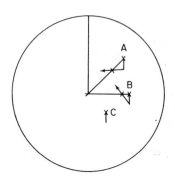

Target 'A' collision in 12 minutes.
Target 'B' collision in 24 minutes.
Target 'C' same course and speed.

Relative motion course 000° speed 12 knots

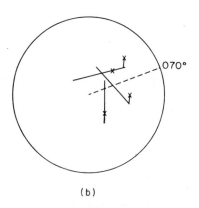

(b)

Computer solution, alter course 70° to starboard and reduce speed to 1 knot, CPA 1.75 miles.

Relative motion after alteration of course and reduction of speed

Fig. 5(b)

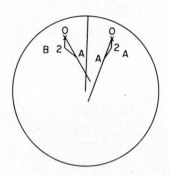

Target 'A' N.A. O.65 mile in 7.8 minutes.
Target 'B' N. A. O.96 mile in 7.6 minutes.

Relative motion

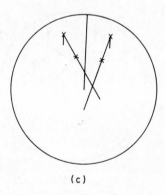

(c)

Computer solution "Stand on" (This is the correct solution).

Fig. 5(c)

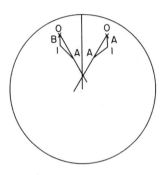

Target 'A' N.A. O.8 mile in 7.75 minutes.
Target 'B' N. A. O.9 mile in 7.6 minutes.

Relative motion course 000° 12 knots

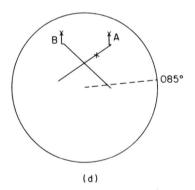

(d)

Computer solution alter 85° to starboard and reduce speed to
2 knots, CPA 1.75 miles.

Relative motion after alteration of course and reduction of
speed

Fig. 5(d)

THE USE OF NUMERICAL MODELS OF TIDE AND SURGE PROPAGATION AS AN AID TO NAVIGATION

D. Prandle

(Institute of Oceanographic Sciences)

INTRODUCTION

A number of numerical models of various sections of the North Sea have been developed primarily for flood prediction. These models simulate both the propagation of the astronomical tide and the generation and propagation of storm surges. The tides effectively originate in the deep ocean and their propagation into these shallow seas can be simulated for an almost infinite period ahead. Surges are generated by the action of wind and pressure gradients, particularly over the shallow sea regions in the northern and central North Sea.

One of the models used for flood forecasting extends over the whole of the continental shelf which surrounds the British Isles. This model simulates the mechanisms of surge generation directly by incorporating the pressure distribution computed by the atmospheric model of the British Meteorological Office. Alternatively, a smaller scale model of the southern North Sea (Fig. 1) may be used with surge data input along the open sea boundaries from actual observations and with the local wind component specified from a weather forecast. These models can provide sea level forecasts up to 24 hours in advance; for shorter term forecasts, up to 6 hours in advance, the accuracy of these forecasts is within ±0.2m.

The logistical problems of using the models for routine flood forecasting along the east coast of Britain are now being investigated. It is envisaged that the models will be in in operation continuously, providing up-dated forecasts perhaps every 6 hours. The computer requirements are relatively small, of the order of less than 1 hour per day for a large machine. In addition, the facilities for monitoring sea-level in real-time already exist and are used by the Storm Tide Warning Service located at the Meteorological Office in Bracknell.

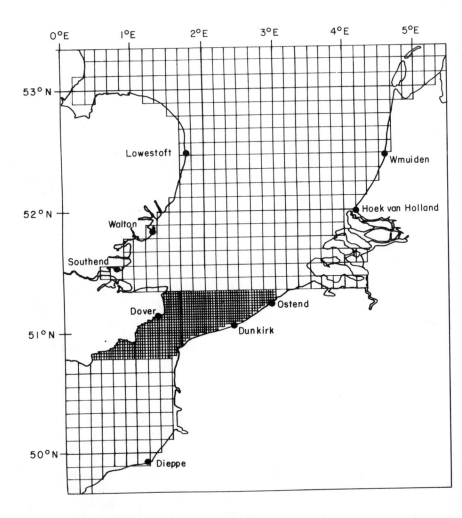

Fig. 1.   Schematic representation of the Southern North Sea

The question now raised is whether the output from the models
could be used for navigational purposes as well as for flood
warning. In the navigational application it is proposed that
model output could be relayed in chart form in the manner used
to relay weather maps. This paper discusses briefly the basis
of the hydrodynamical models and illustrates some examples of
the type of model output that might be appropriate.

NUMERICAL MODEL

The results shown in this paper were obtained from the
model shown in Fig. 1 consisting of a combined model of the
southern North Sea and River Thames and including a detailed
representation of the Dover Strait. The model uses an explicit
finite difference scheme for solving, by means of a forward
time-stepping procedure, the relevant equations of motion
(Prandle 1974).

The hydrodynamic equations are expressed for space coordinates along lines of latitude and longitude as follows:

$$\frac{\partial u}{\partial t} + u\frac{\partial u}{\partial x} + v\frac{\partial u}{\partial y} + g\frac{\partial Z}{\partial x} + \frac{\partial P}{\rho\partial x} - \frac{F_x}{\rho(D+Z)} + gC_0\frac{u(u^2+v^2)^{\frac{1}{2}}}{(D+Z)} - \Omega v = 0 \quad (1)$$

$$\frac{\partial v}{\partial t} + u\frac{\partial v}{\partial x} + v\frac{\partial v}{\partial y} + g\frac{\partial Z}{\partial y} + \frac{\partial P}{\rho\partial y} - \frac{G_y}{\rho(D+Z)} + gC_0\frac{v(u^2+v^2)^{\frac{1}{2}}}{(D+Z)} + \Omega u = 0 \quad (2)$$

$$\frac{\partial Z}{\partial t} + \frac{\partial}{\partial x}(u(D+Z)) + \frac{1}{\Delta x}\frac{\partial}{\partial y}(v(D+Z)\Delta x) = 0 \quad (3)$$

where u,v   are depth mean velocities along the x and y axes,
               respectively,
       x,y   orthogonal axes positive to the east and to the
               north,
       t   time,
       g   gravitational constant,
       Z   elevation of the water surface above a horizontal
               datum,
       D   depth of the bed below the same datum,
       P   atmospheric pressure,
       ρ density of water,
       F_x,G_y wind stress in the x and y directions,
       C_0 bed friction coefficient,
       Ω Coriolis parameter
       Δx grid length in the x direction.

I

At the open sea boundaries the elevation Z is prescribed
and at land boundaries the velocity orthogonal to the boundar
is set to zero. In simulating the effect of a storm surge
the wind stress terms F_x and G_y are calculated directly from
a knowledge of the wind speed and direction; similarly the
pressure gradient may be specified directly.

MODEL OUTPUT

The results shown in Figs. 2, 3 and 4 are intended to
illustrate how the model may be used as an aid to navigation
and hence the details of the conditions associated with these
results are omitted.

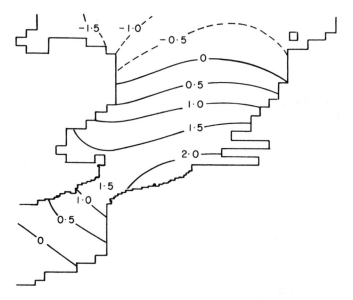

Fig. 2(a)   Tidal heights in metres at 0300, 1st February 1953

Fig. 2(a) shows the distribution of tidal heights as
computed for 03.00, 1st February 1953; Fig. 2(b) shows the
computed heights for tide plus surge at that same time. The
heights shown refer to the level of the sea surface above a
fixed horizontal plane which for practical purposes may be
regarded as mean sea level. Provision of tidal information
in this form should enable shipping to make full use of
available water depths and also clearly indicate the extent
of the reduction in depths on the falling tide. Contour

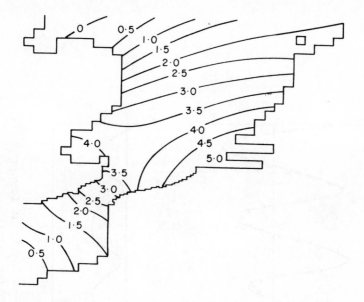

Fig. 2(b)   Heights for tide plus surge in metres at 0300,
1st February 1953

diagrams of this type can be produced automatically in a matter
of seconds using any standard computer line printer.

The combined tide plus surge heights shown in Fig. 2(b)
were obtained from a simulation of the disastrous storm of
1953 studied in detail by Prandle (1975). This example shows
the possible extent of storm surges in this region, a comparison of Figs. 2(a) and (b) indicates that surges may increase
tidal heights by more than 2.5m - perhaps of more concern is
that surges may likewise decrease tidal heights to the same
extent. This modification to tidal levels is illustrated in
the time-series for surface elevation at Dover shown in Fig. 3
for the duration of the 1953 surge. This figure also demonstrates the accuracy of the computed levels by the comparison
shown with the corresponding recorded values.

In addition to providing computed values of sea levels
the models can also provide, in graphical form, the direction
and speed of tidal currents for each grid square. The usefulness of such information is indicated by the time-series for
the flow of water through the Dover Strait shown in Fig. 3
for the duration of the 1953 surge. This time-series shows

Prandle

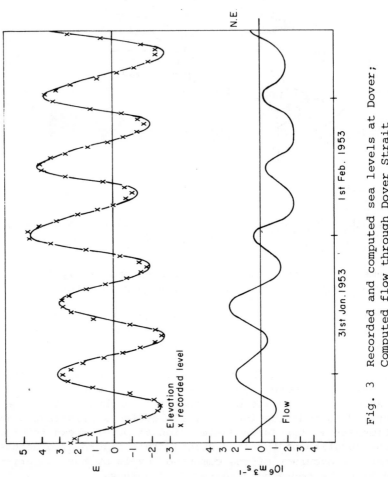

Fig. 3   Recorded and computed sea levels at Dover;
         Computed flow through Dover Strait

that a storm may change the normal flood and ebb currents to
such an extent that the currents may continue in one direction
for over 24 hours.

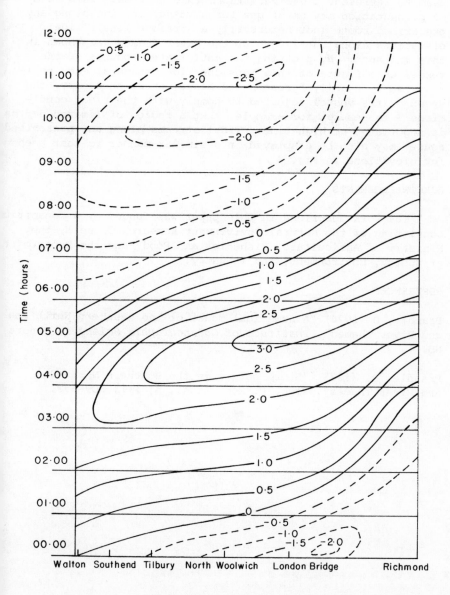

Fig. 4 Computed tidal levels in metres along the River Thames
for 19th October 1970

An alternative method of displaying tidal elevations to that used in Figs. 2(a) and (b) is shown in Fig. 4 where the spatial information is limited to one dimension with the other used to represent tidal variations through time. This form of presentation may be of use for a vessel sailing along any prescribed route (not necessarily a straight line); tidal elevations along the length of the River Thames are shown in this instance. By plotting the anticipated course of the vessel on a figure of this type the tidal stage at each position can be readily foreseen and hence, where necessary, the speed of the vessel adjusted to comply with the tidal conditions - to ensure, for example, that a region of limited depths is negotiated at high tide. Tidal streams along any prescribed route may also be displayed in a similar manner to that used for elevations in Fig. 4.

ACKNOWLEDGEMENTS

The work described in this paper was funded by a Consortium consisting of the Natural Environment Research Council, the Ministry of Agriculture, Fisheries and Food, and the Department of Energy, Environment, and Industry.

REFERENCES

Prandle, D (1974) "A numerical model of the southern North Sea and River Thames", *Institute of Oceanographic Sciences*, Report No. **4**, 25.

Prandle, D. (1975) "Storm surges in the southern North Sea and River Thames", *Proc. R. Soc. Lond.*, A, **344**, 509-539.

SHIPPING OPERATIONS IN THE SUEZ CANAL

J.D. Griffiths and E.M. Hassan

(University of Wales Institute of Science and Technology)

1. INTRODUCTION

Apart from roads, canals were Man's earliest attempt to facilitate the transport of goods within a land mass. As early as the 5th Century BC the Chinese had begun work on the Grand Canal of China between Hangchow and Peking, which with a total length of 1000 miles is said to be the longest, as well as the oldest, existing canal in the world.

The idea of constructing a waterway connecting the Red and Mediterranean Seas dates back 4000 years, and there still remains evidence of several olden-day canals which utilised a tributary of the Nile as access from the Mediterranean Sea to a point north of Cairo together with a man-made waterway cut eastwards towards the Red Sea. Although such canals appear to have been in use for substantial periods of time, they were eventually abandoned because of the high level of siltation which occurred.

The present Suez Canal was constructed under the direction of the French engineer and diplomat Ferdinand de Lesseps. Excavations started on 25th April, 1859, and the Canal was first opened to navigation on 17th November, 1869. A fascinating account of the construction of the Canal is given by Burchell and Issawi (1966). The Canal remained open continuously until the Middle-East war of 1967, apart from short periods of closure during World Wars I and II and in 1956 when it was nationalised by Egypt. Because of the extensive damage caused by the Arab-Israeli wars over the period 1967-73, it was feared that the Canal would never re-open. However, following extensive salvage and clearance operations by the British, French, US and Egyptian Navies, the Suez Canal was again opened to the ships of the world on 5th June, 1975, eight years to the day from its closure.

2. GENERAL INFORMATION

The Suez Canal lies on the shortest navigable route between the Eastern and Western worlds. Typical savings in distances compared with the alternative route via the Cape of Good Hope are: Tokyo to Rotterdam 25%, Arabian Gulf to London 45%, Bombay to Odessa 65%. Reductions in the cost of transport are usually of the order of 35% to 50%.

The length of the Canal, measured from the lighthouse in Port Said harbour to the signal station at Port Tewfik, is 160.3 km of which about 121 km may be said to belong to the Canal proper with the remainder lying in the Bitter Lakes. The width of the Canal at water level varies between 180 and 200 metres, and the buoys which indicate the navigable channel define a width of about 110 metres. Such a width is not sufficient to allow ships to pass or overtake one another, and a convoy system is used for transit of vessels (see Section 4). At present the minimum depth of the Canal allows tankers of dead-weight-tonnage (d.w.t.) up to 60 000 to transit fully laden, and tankers up to 100 000 d.w.t. to transit in a partially loaded condition. Supertankers up to 250 000 d.w.t. are able to transit in ballast condition.

During 1966, the last full year of operation prior to closure, 21 250 vessels passed through the Canal, with the volume of trade amounting to 240 million tonnes. This volume represented nearly 14% of goods transported by sea throughout the world: 176 million tonnes of oil were transported through the Canal (19% of the world total), including 36% of all oil supplied from the Arabian Gulf. During the years prior to closure the average number of daily transits rose steadily from 41 in 1955 to 58 in 1966. The highest number of ships ever registered in a day stands at 84, which occurred on 9th March, 1958.

The over-all cost to world economy of the Canal closure is estimated to be 1700 million dollars per annum, mainly resulting from increased transport costs. The total losses sustained by the Suez Canal Authority (SCA), including revenues, dues, damage, during the 8 year period of closure is estimated to be 3600 million dollars. Present revenues are of the order of 1 million dollars per day.

3.   DEVELOPMENT OF THE CANAL

Up until the time of nationalisation in 1956, the physical limitations of the Canal had greatly influenced world ship-owners with regard to the sizes of ships built, particularly those of oil tankers. Following nationalisation, in an era of cheap oil and transport costs, ship-owners took the initiative and began to build large tankers. Mindful of the effect that such changes would have on the tonnage of oil transported through the Canal, the Suez Canal Authority began a programme of expansion in 1958 which was to be executed in two stages. The first stage was completed by February, 1964 and consisted of widening and deepening the Canal so that ships with draughts of 38 ft could be accommodated, thus allowing vessels of 60 000 d.w.t. to transit fully loaded· The second stage of development was intended to deepen the Canal to accept vessels of draughts up to 40 ft, corresponding to ships of 70 000 d.w.t. This work was scheduled to be completed by the end of 1967, but the project was not finished because of the start of the Arab-Israeli war.

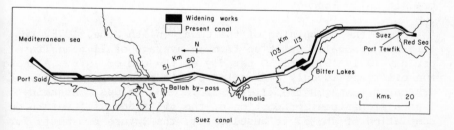

Fig. 1 Suez Canal

Despite these development plans, the increase in the sizes
of tankers being constructed outstripped the enlargement work
in the Canal. For example, as early as 1963 some vessels in
the range 70 000 to 110 000 d.w.t. came into service. Further
it became apparent that shipyards were not increasing the size
of tankers in a gradual manner. By the mid-1960's tankers in
the range 200 000 to 250 000 d.w.t. were being built, and this
led to revision of the SCA plans already being undertaken.
In July 1966 it was announced that the Canal would be develope
so as to allow tankers of 200 000 d.w.t. to transit fully lade
Work on this development in fact began in February, 1967, but
was soon to be halted because of the Middle-East war. It is
interesting to note that at closure 74% of the world tanker
d.w.t. was able to transit the Canal, whereas at the re-openir
in 1975 only 27% of the world fleet could use the Canal. In
the 8 years of closure, supertankers or VLCC's (Very Large
Crude Carriers) had become dominant in oil transport.

Faced with this situation on re-opening, the SCA had littl
option but to attempt to win back the lucrative oil trade by
expanding the Canal still further to cater for supertankers.
Shortly after the successful re-opening, SCA announced plans
to enlarge the Canal to allow vessels of 53 ft draught, corresponding to 150 000 d.w.t., to transit fully loaded. This
project is now well under way and is scheduled for completion
by the end of 1979. Approximately 50% of the world tanker
tonnage will then be able to use the Canal in fully laden
condition, and practically the whole world fleet will be able
to transit in ballast. Further development is planned from
1980 enabling vessels of 67 ft draught (250 000 d.w.t.) to
transit fully loaded.

Since the re-opening of the Canal on 5th June, 1975, traffic has gradually built up from an average of 21 transits
per day (July 1975) to 50 per day at the end of 1976. Althoug
the oil trade is only a fraction of its pre-closure level,
dry cargo tonnages are already above 1967 values. Assuming
that a significant proportion of the oil trade will return on
completion of the 53 ft development, the future prospects for
the Suez Canal appear to be extremely bright.

Against the background of changing attitudes in the shipping world, the Suez Canal Authority sought international advice on the future prospects for the Canal. Late in 1975 the
British firm of consulting engineers, Maunsell Consultants Lt
were awarded a feasibility study by SCA, and because of the

wide ranging nature of the project Maunsell's formed a consortium to investigate the various aspects of the problem. Further details of the over-all study may be found in Sewell (1976) and Griffiths (1977).

This paper considers one of the most important factors of the study - that of estimating the maximum number of ships per day which can be processed by the Suez Canal. The importance of accurate estimation of the shipping capacity, both in terms of ships already able to transit the Canal and also in terms of those which will be accommodated when the development plans outlined in Section 3 are completed, cannot be over-emphasised, since SCA have to make provision for increasing the capacity in line with levels of traffic forecast for the future. For example, one method of increasing the capacity (see Section 6) is to provide additional by-passes, thus dualling the Canal over greater lengths than at present. Needless to say the capital costs of such schemes are substantial, and incorrect estimates of capacity could lead to premature, or conversely belated, decisions on the timings of such expansions.

In order to understand the difficulties involved in determining the shipping capacity it is necessary to consider in a little more detail the traffic system which operates in the Canal.

4.   THE TRAFFIC SYSTEM IN THE CANAL

The major lengths of the Canal allow only one-way passages of ships, but vessels are allowed to pass one another in two sections, at Bitter Lakes between km 101 and 116 and at Ballah-by-pass between km 51 and 60. The movement of ships is organised in convoys.

The convoy system in operation prior to closure of the Canal in 1967 utilised three convoys per day, two southbound and one northbound. In this system the first southbound convoy starts from Port Said at 2300 hours, and the northbound from Port Tewfik at 0500 hours. These starting times enable the convoys to pass one another in the Bitter Lakes, with the northbound convoy having a non-stop daylight passage as far as is possible. This latter condition is desirable on safety grounds, since the northbound convoy includes tankers carrying crude oil and other dangerous cargoes. The second southbound convoy starts from Port Said at 0700 hours and proceeds to Ballah where it ties up in the western loop of the by-pass to allow the northbound convoy to pass. The second southbound

256   Griffiths and Hassan

convoy then travels non-stop from Ballah to Port Tewfik.

Navigation of vessels by SCA pilots is compulsory from the waiting areas lying off each end of the Canal until their exit to open sea at the opposite end. Each ship has to enter the Canal at a specified time in order to take its place in the convoy, and must maintain certain speeds and separation distances from the vessel ahead throughout its passage. The speeds at which convoys are allowed to transit various sections of the Canal are laid down in the Regulations and Schedules of the SCA. A pilot is able to judge accurately the speed of his ship by timing its passage between the 200 metre or kilometre boards situated on the banks of the Canal. The Signal Stations record the times at which ships pass, and relay the information to the Movement Control Office at Ismailia. The progress of each vessel is recorded by the Movement Controllers on a chart known as a Transit Graph. In this way it is possible for the Controllers to gain an over-all view of the progression of the convoys, and to ensure that speeds and separation distances of vessels are maintained at the specified levels. In the event of a ship having to stop due to engine breakdown, steering failure, bad weather, or other cause, the pilot immediately informs the Movement Control Office and messages are relayed to all following ships commanding them to halt and tie up at the nearest mooring bollard. It should be appreciated that the physical process of bringing a ship to rest from a speed of about 14 km per hour in a confined waterway is not an easy one, and depending on the size of the vessel can take several kilometres. The specified separation distances take account of such factors as the size of ship and type of cargo carried. Naturally vessels carrying petroleum products or other potentially dangerous cargoes are required to maintain larger separation distances than say general cargo ships. For example, two general cargo ships would have a minimum interval of 5 minutes (about 1 km) between them, while a vessel carrying fissile material would be required to be separated by 20 minutes (about 4 km) from the vessels ahead and astern.

The allowed speed of a convoy varies between 12 and 14 km per hour, and is determined by a number of factors. Foremost, the speed is restricted so that the wake from a vessel does not cause damage to the banks of the Canal. Bank erosion is an important consideration and is influenced to a significant extent by the design of the ship. Certain types of vessel cause little wash and are unable to steer adequately unless

travelling at a speed higher than laid down by SCA; such vessels
are usually placed at the head of the convoy. Another factor
which influences convoy speeds is the force of the current,
particularly that prevailing in the southern part of the Canal;
speeds relative to the ground are adjusted to take account of
such conditions.

A diagrammatic representation of a Transit Graph is shown
in Fig. 2. The indicated speeds may be increased or decreased
by 1 km per hour by permission from the Movement Control Office.
Analysis of a substantial amount of data collected at Ismailia
shows that significantly higher speeds are often apparent.

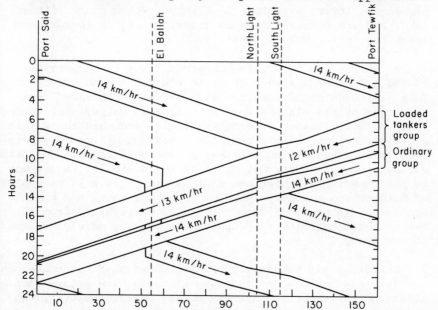

Fig. 2   A transit graph for ships moving through the canal.
Graphs of this kind allow the movement controllers a
complete picture of the situation over   the whole
160 km of the Canal

It will be noted from Fig. 2 that the northbound convoy
consists of two distinct classes. The first group consists
of loaded tankers, while general cargo ships form the major
part of the second group, although certain other types of
vessel are also included, e.g. towed barges, floating cranes.
The main reason for creating separate classes of vessels is
the desirability of allowing loaded tankers a straight-through
passage. Experience has shown tankers to have a better record

of reliability than general cargo vessels. By placing general
cargo ships at the rear of the convoy, tankers are not so
likely to be hindered by the breakdown of a vessel ahead, and
the danger of collision is reduced. Since the first group is
obliged to travel at a relatively lower mean speed than the
second group, a gap of about 1 hour is imposed between the
groups at Port Tewfik and on departure from Bitter Lakes.
This enables the second group to travel at a speed consistent
with good steering characteristics without overtaking the first
group. At present SCA are experimenting with a third group
of vessels, designated "fast ships", which transit ahead of
the loaded tankers. This group consists of vessels such as
container ships, auto-carriers, roll on - roll off ships,
passenger liners, warships, lash ships, which cause little
wake, and are hence allowed to travel at higher speeds than
specified in the SCA regulations.

As far as the future is concerned, it will be necessary
to add a further distinct group to the northbound convoy.
This will consist of supertankers, and it is intended that
the order of the classes will be: (i) fast ships, (ii) loaded
tankers, (iii) loaded supertankers, (iv) ordinary ships. It
was mentioned previously that the behaviour of loaded supertankers in a restricted waterway is not well known. Following
guidance from the National Maritime Institute, it is assumed
in the capacity calculations that supertankers will be capable
of maintaining a convoy speed of 13 km per hour, and that a
separation interval of 30 minutes will be required from the
vessel ahead to allow the supertanker to stop safely in case
of emergency.

Griffiths and Hassan (1977) have shown that the consequence
of these assumptions are that supertankers have a far-reaching
effect on the shipping capacity of the Canal. However, the
reduction in capacity as far as the number of transits per
day is concerned is offset by the increase in cargo tonnage
which is achieved by the use of the larger vessels.

5. THE THEORETICAL CAPACITY OF THE PRESENT CANAL

Traditionally the shipping capacity of the Canal has been
measured in terms of the number of vessels which are able to
complete their transits during a 24-hour period. Many factors
affect this measure; these include:

(i)   the division of the total number of ships between the
       northbound and southbound convoys;

(ii)   the convoy system adopted in the Canal;
(iii) the speeds at which ships are allowed to transit, and
       the time gaps required between them at various nodes
       of the Canal;
(iv)   the mix of different categories of ships which transit
       the Canal.

In this section the "theoretical" capacity of the present
Canal is determined in terms of "standard ships". A standard
ship is defined to be one which transits the Canal at a speed
of 14 km per hour and which is separated from the vessel ahead
and astern by a gap of 10 minutes.

In calculating the shipping capacity the following assumptions are made.

(a) A three-convoy per day system is in operation: one north-
     bound and two southbound.
(b) The northbound convoy does not stop while transitting the
     Canal (see Section 4).
(c) The number of ships transitting the Canal is equally
     divided between northbound and southbound convoys. (Records
     show that slightly more ships pass southwards than north-
     wards).

In addition the following features relating to the physical
layout of the Canal and its operating system must be taken
into account.

(d) The storage capacity of El-Ballah-by-Pass (between km 51
     km 60) is 17 ships for the second southbound convoy.
(e) The storage capacity of Bitter Lakes (between North-Light -
     km 103.4 - and South-Light - km 112.9) is 36 ships for
     the first southbound convoy.
(f) Southbound convoys begin transitting the Canal from Port
     Said at km 3.7, and end their transits at Port Tewfik at
     km 160.3.
(g) The northbound convoy begins its transit of the Canal at
     Port Tewfik at km 160.3 and finishes at Port Said at km 0.
(h) The gap between the last ship of the second southbound
     convoy arriving at Port Tewfik (km 160.3) and the first
     ship of the northbound convoy leaving Port Tewfik should
     be at least 30 minutes, so that the waiting area at Suez
     Bay can be cleared by the southbound convoy before the
     northbound convoy begins its transit through the Canal.
(i) The first ship of the northbound convoy may cross the
     last ship of the first southbound convoy at km 101. The

last ship of the northbound convoy may cross the first
ship of the first southbound convoy at km 116.

(j)   The last ship of the northbound convoy may cross the first
ship of the second southbound convoy at El-Ballah south
(km 60).

The following notation is used:

l = the number of standard ships in the northbound convoy;

q = the number of standard ships in the first southbound convoy

r = the number of standard ships in the second southbound convo

Taking into account the speed characteristics and crossing
points of ships, the problem turns out to be a simple integer
linear programming one, where it is required to maximise
$l + q + r$ subject to the following constraints:

$$l = q + r \qquad\qquad\qquad (5.1)$$

$$q = 61 - l \qquad\qquad\qquad (5.2)$$

$$r \leqslant 17 \qquad\qquad\qquad\quad (5.3)$$

$$q \leqslant 36 \qquad\qquad\qquad\quad (5.4)$$

$$r + l \leqslant 57 \qquad\qquad\qquad (5.5)$$

$$l > 0, \; q > 0, \; r > 0. \qquad\qquad (5.6)$$

By solving this programming problem, the maximum theoretical capacity of the Suez Canal can be shown to be 78 standard
ships with $l = 39$, $q = 22$ and $r = 17$.   Fig. 3 is the transit
graph showing how this capacity is achieved.

In order to convert the above theoretical capacity from
standard ships to real ships, it was necessary to find how the
performances of real vessels compare with those assumed for
standard ships.   To this end a substantial amount of data was
collected from the Canal Zone relating to such factors as
speeds and separation distances of different types of vessels
at several positions along the Canal.

The conversion procedure is complex because of the number
of factors involved (Griffiths and Hassan (1977)).   The most
significant result is the dramatic effect that the introductio
of supertankers will have on the capacity of the Canal.   For
example, when about 30% of the northbound traffic consists of
supertankers - a situation forecast for the early 1980's - the

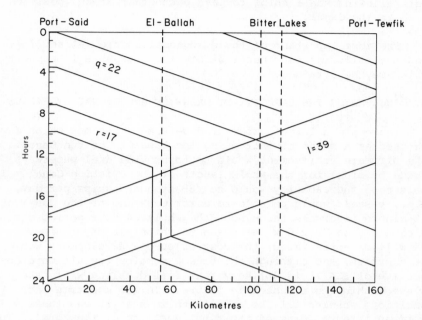

Fig. 3 The Theoretical Maximum Capacity of The Suez Canal

actual capacity of the Canal would be about 50 vessels per day.

For the remainder of this paper, in order to make reasonable comparisons, we shall consider capacity to be measured in terms of standard ships. Forecasts indicate that the present capacity will be exceeded in the early 1980's, and that by 1990 the average number of vessels wishing to transit will exceed 90 (standard ships) per day. It is thus clear that urgent steps must be taken to increase the capacity of the Canal, such increases being closely linked to the plans for enlarging the Canal to accommodate supertankers (see Section 3) and to forecasts of future traffic.

There are several ways in which the capacity of the Canal may be increased; these include:

(a) building additional by-passes so that opposing convoys may pass each other over greater distances than at present;

(b) changing the mode of operation of traffic; in particular, by increasing the cycle time from 24 hours;

(c) permitting increased speeds of transit and/or reduced separation distances between vessels in a convoy;

(d)   allowing small ships to pass each other at any position
       in the Canal.

The most important of these suggestions are (a) and (b),
and the following sections indicate the increases in capacity
which may be attained.

6.   INCREASING THE CAPACITY BY MEANS OF ADDITIONAL BY-PASSES

There are a large number of development schemes which may
be used as a means of increasing the capacity of the Canal.
The ultimate achievement would be to provide dual waterways
(side by side) for the whole length of the existing Canal.   In
this case the capacity would be 288 standard ships per day,
i.e., vessels would be able to enter each end of the Canal at
10 minute intervals throughout the whole 24 hour period giving
a capacity of (2 x 6 x 24) standard ships per day.   However,
as will be appreciated, the cost of such a development would
be enormous, and although the scheme remains the ultimate objective of SCA it is unlikely that full dualling will take
place within the foreseeable future.   In the meantime less
ambitious schemes will be undertaken in stages, and these will
form an integral part of the final dualling of the Canal.   The
capacities achievable with three of these developments are now
discussed.   It should be emphasised that these schemes have
been proposed not only from the point of view of increasing
the capacity but also for various operational and engineering
reasons.

Scheme 1

A by-pass (to be known as the Port Fouad By-Pass) would be
constructed at the northern end of the Canal in order to provide direct exit to the Mediterranean Sea from a point near
km 12 in the Canal, thus enabling vessels to avoid the congestion of Port Said harbour.   This effectively reduces the over-
all length of the Canal by 12 km.   In addition a by-pass would
be built to the north of Lake Timsah between km 73 and 86, and
southbound vessels would be able to moor in the Lake to allow
northbound vessels to pass.   The storage capacity at Lake
Timsah would be 20 standard ships.

This situation allows an additional southbound convoy to
be added to the operational system described in Section 4.
Fig. 4 shows the details of the system, with the new southbound
convoy travelling to Timsah By-Pass and waiting until the last
vessel of the northbound convoy has passed km 86 before it

proceeds directly to Port Tewfik.

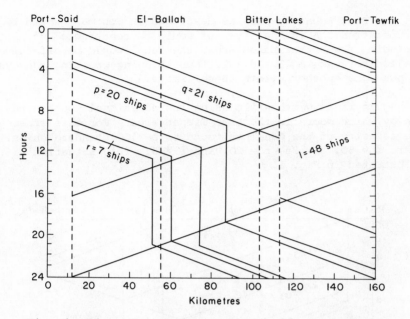

Fig. 4   Scheme 1.   Maximum Capacity 96 standard ships

Using the same notation as in Section 5, and letting p be the number of standard ships in the new southbound convoy, the problem is to maximise $\ell + q + p + r$ subject to the following constraints:

$$\ell = q + r + p \qquad\qquad (6.1)$$

$$q = 68 - \ell \qquad\qquad (6.2)$$

$$r \leqslant 17 \qquad\qquad (6.3)$$

$$q \leqslant 36 \qquad\qquad (6.4)$$

$$p \leqslant 20 \qquad\qquad (6.5)$$

$$r \leqslant 55 - \ell \qquad\qquad (6.6)$$

$$\ell > 0, \quad q > 0, \quad p > 0, \quad r > 0 \qquad\qquad (6.7)$$

Solving this integer programming problem, the capacity of this scheme is found to be 96 standard ships, with $\ell = 48$, $q = 21$, $p = 20$, and $r = 7$. Fig. 4 illustrates how this capacity is achieved.

Scheme 2

The Port Fouad By-pass as described in Scheme 1 would be in operation. A further by-pass would be constructed so that, including the Bitter Lakes area, the Canal would be effectively dualled between km 73 and 122, thus allowing opposing convoys to pass one another within these limits.

Again it is worth-while using the additional southbound convoy which moors in the Lake Timsah area. For this scheme the capacity of the Canal is found to be 100 standard ships, where ℓ = 50, q = 25, p = 20, and r = 5. This situation is illustrated in Fig. 5.

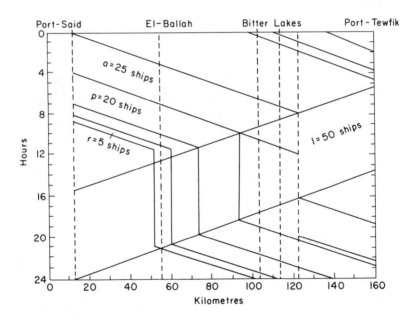

Fig. 5   Scheme 2.   Maximum Capacity 100 standard ships

Scheme 3

As before the Port Fouad By-pass would be in operation, but in addition there would be a continuous section of dual Canal between km 51 and 131. In this case it is necessary to use only one convoy per day in each direction, as shown in Fig. 6. The capacity of this scheme is 112 standard ships per day.

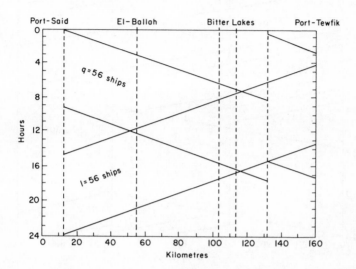

Fig. 6   Scheme 3.   Maximum Capacity 112 standard ships

7.   INCREASING THE CAPACITY BY ALTERING THE CYCLE TIME

We define the cycle time of operations as the interval between the departure times from Port Said of successive first southbound convoys, i.e., the cycle time is the period elapsing before the set of operations repeats itself.   Figs. 1 to 5 illustrate operations of the Canal based on a 24-hour cycle. It may be observed from these diagrams that for quite substantial periods of time any given point of the Canal will have no convoy passing.   For example, from Fig. 2 at km 30 there are no vessels passing for about 11 of the 24 hours available, representing a proportion of about 45% of the cycle.   It would be clearly more efficient if this "dead time" were to be spread over a longer period than 24 hours.   This gives rise to the idea of increasing the cycle time.   It is shown below that this change in operational procedure can produce a dramatic increase in the shipping capacity.   A major advantage of this method of increasing the capacity is that it has no capital cost associated with it, this being in direct contrast to the schemes discussed in Section 6 which require massive capital investment.

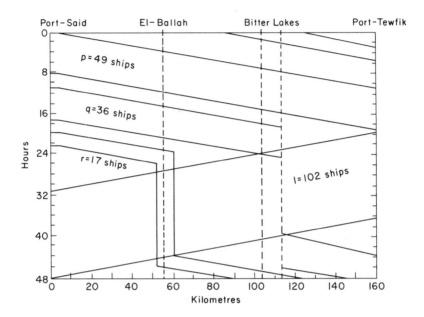

Fig. 7   Cycle time 48 hours.   Maximum capacity 204 standard
ships

        To illustrate the effect of increasing the cycle time
from 24 hours we consider a situation where a 48-hour cycle
is used in the existing Canal.   Fig. 7 shows how it is possibl
to accommodate 204 standard ships in the 48 hour period,
giving a capacity of 102 standard ships per 24 hours.   A
feature of the convoy system used is the introduction of a
southbound convoy having non-stop passage from Port Said to
Port Tewfik.   It should be noted that in this case the amount
of "dead time" at any point in the Canal has been substantiall
reduced when expressed as a proportion of the cycle time.
For example, at km 30 the total length of time when there are
no vessels passing this point is a little over 14 hours,
representing less than 30% of the cycle time.

        When supertankers are introduced to the Canal it will be
necessary to enlarge the Bitter Lakes area to allow these
vessels to tie up safely in cases of emergency, e.g. breakdown
of a vessel ahead, bad weather or accidents.   This means that
the storage capacity of the Bitter Lakes will not be restricte
to 36 standard ships as postulated in equation (5.4).   Removal

of this constraint results in a further increase in capacity
to 111 standard ships per 24 hours, which is comparable with
the best of the schemes discussed in Section 5.

There is no reason, of course, why the cycle time
should be fixed at 48 hours. In general for an n-day cycle,
where n is not necessarily an integer, the capacity using a
three convoy system as shown in Fig. 2 is given by
$(144 - \frac{66}{n})$ standard ships per 24 hours. This follows from
solution of the following programming problem:

Maximise $\ell + q + r$

subject to

$$\ell = q + r \qquad\qquad (7.1)$$

$$q = 144n - 83 - \ell \qquad\qquad (7.2)$$

$$r \leqslant 17 \qquad\qquad (7.3)$$

$$r \leqslant 144n - 87 - \ell \qquad\qquad (7.4)$$

Fig. 8 is a graphical representation of the relationship
between capacity and cycle times. It should be noted that
the increase in capacity tails off rapidly for cycle times
greater than 2 days.

From the above comments it appears highly advantageous
to increase the cycle time from 24 hours if we wish to increase
the capacity of the Canal. However such a proposal has a
number of disadvantages associated with it from an operational
viewpoint. For example, if a 36 or 48-hour cycle were to be
used, vessels arriving at either end of the Canal would not
know precisely when the next convoy would be leaving; this
is in contrast to the present system where it is known that
convoys depart at specified times each day and vessels can
arrange their arrival times at the Canal to take best advantage
of the situation. Clearly if vessels turn up at random with
a 48-hour cycle operating, there could be substantial delays
before they join the next available convoy. However, various
methods of counteracting such disadvantages have been considered
(for example, a time-table could be circulated to the shipping
world based on a 36 or 48-hour cycle), and it is confidently
expected that most objections to an operational system having
a 48-hour cycle could be overcome.

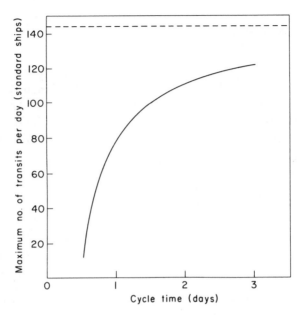

Fig. 8 Graph of relationship between capacity and cycle time

A full queueing analysis of the system has also been undertaken, and it is intended to report on this aspect of the problem elsewhere at a later date.

8. CONCLUSIONS

Estimating the shipping capacity of the Suez Canal is a complex procedure depending on a large number of factors. For comparison purposes the capacities of the existing Canal and its proposed developments have been calculated in terms of standard ships. To cater for the levels of traffic fore-cast for the next 20 years or so it is probably necessary to raise the shipping capacity to a figure in excess of 100 standard ships per day. It has been shown that this may be achieved by constructing additional by-passes to provide greater lengths of dual waterway. The most ambitious of these schemes raises the capacity to 112 standard ships per day. An alternative method of increasing the capacity, with little change to the physical layout of the Canal, is to expand the cycle time of operations from the present 24 hours. This simple expedient raises the capacity to 111 standard ships per day, with the advantage of little capital expenditure.

9. ACKNOWLEDGEMENT

The authors wish to thank Maunsell Consultants Ltd. for providing the opportunity to undertake this study and for their permission to present this paper. The opinions expressed in the paper, however, are those of the authors and are not necessarily in concurrence with those of Maunsell's.

10. REFERENCES

Burchell, S. C., Issawi, C., "Building the Suez Canal", Cassel, 1966.

Griffiths, J. D. "The Development of the Suez Canal", *Maritime Policy and Management*, **4**, No. 3, 1977, pp. 155-161.

Griffiths, J. D., Hassan, E. M. "The Maximum Shipping Capacity of the Suez Canal", *Maritime Policy and Management*, **4**, No. 4, 1977, pp. 303-317.

Sewell, T. F. D. "Towards New Transit Regulations on an Enlarged Canal", *The Dock and Harbour Authority*, July, 1976, pp. 80-82.